The
FARM CHEMURGIC

BY THE SAME AUTHOR
CHEMISTRY TRIUMPHANT
(WILLIAMS & WILKINS, BALTIMORE)

The
FARM CHEMURGIC

FARMWARD THE STAR OF
DESTINY LIGHTS OUR WAY

By

WILLIAM J. HALE, Ph.D.
RESEARCH CONSULTANT
THE DOW CHEMICAL COMPANY

ST. MARY'S COLLEGE LIBRARY
WINONA, MINN.

THE STRATFORD COMPANY
PUBLISHERS, BOSTON, MASS.

COPYRIGHT —— 1934 —— BY
THE STRATFORD COMPANY
Publishers
PRINTED IN THE UNITED STATES OF AMERICA

PRINTED BY
THE ALPINE PRESS, INC., BOSTON, MASS.

To

THE MEMORY OF

HELEN

Table of Contents

	Preface	i
I.	The Chemical Revolution	1
II.	Intense Nationalism	19
III.	Property Valuation	32
IV.	Property Taxation	44
V.	The Four Horsemen	57
VI.	Chemical Life Cycles	77
VII.	The Wreck of the Farm Cycle	90
VIII.	The Wreck of the National Cycle	102
IX.	The Ship of State Adrift	115
X.	Chemi-Biological Reckoning	128
XI.	Chemurgy to the Fore	141
XII.	Science at the Helm	156
XIII.	The Old Order Changeth	170
XIV.	Clouds Roll Away	182
XV.	Full Speed Ahead	192

Preface

THE farm is the foundation of Society. The rise of agriculture in early Neolithic times marks the dawn of civilization. Not until the middle of the nineteenth century do we find a trend downward in utilization of agricultural products; this came through inroads made by mechanical inventions and primarily through developments in metallurgy,—the science of working with and for metals.

Our industrial era took its rise in mass production, chiefly dependent upon mineral resources for raw products. The assurance of strength and lasting qualities in metal structures directed increasing endeavor toward the procurement of raw products from mines at ever lowering costs. The populace was becoming mineral minded.

The fall of agriculture is thus recorded. But the slow and definite rise in organic chemistry, and synthesis of compounds of exceeding stability, has come to arrest this baneful drift. It is the rebirth of agriculture thus destined to carry civilization to a higher plane.

The first step in this transition is the chemical revolution itself,—that change brought about through

THE FARM CHEMURGIC

replacement of nature's chemi-biologically grown products by the products of man's labor. Naturally this revolution took its rise in the spread of chemical knowledge,—the aftermath of the World War.

But man cannot outrun nature; neither can he worst her in her own chemi-biological laboratory, or what we choose to call her chemurgical field. Chemurgy, from the Greek χημεία (black art of Egypt, or chemistry) (chêmi = Egypt) and ἔργον (work) is that science concerned in the working with and for chemical compounds.

The farm is the great chemurgical plant; taking the earth as a whole, far more is accomplished here by nature than by the two billions or more of human inhabitants. In just those countries, as our own, where man has labored to manufacture without recourse to what nature has freely offered of her growth, we find depression. Apparently through adversity is it alone possible for this genus *Homo Sapiens* himself to become sapient.

In the midst of the chemical revolution we were chemically disorganized; in the depths of depression we are chemurgically incapacitated; we have been bent on following those false gods of gold, steel, petroleum, and such, till our eyes are blinded and besmirched and we cannot read the sign before us:—

PREFACE

"This is the road all nations trod ere they met with final destruction."

The Farm holds the key to human happiness. These false gods are but vassals in the chemurgical hands of nature. Production and consumption of worldly goods must be in strict accordance with nature's living output; on such principles we can build and manufacture to our hearts' content and fear no evil. Enlightenment dawns; Elysian fields lie before us; prosperity beckons. The road is the road of Chemurgy, the handmaiden of nature. If we falter and forsake her, chaos alone awaits us.

WILLIAM J. HALE.

Midland, Michigan,
July 4, 1934.

THE FARM CHEMURGIC

CHAPTER I

The Chemical Revolution

FOR thousands of years man had known no other power than his own and that of his servants. The subjugation of human beings had become an adjunct to each succeeding civilization. Through the labor of slaves arose the towers of Babylon, the pyramids of Egypt and the temples of ancient Greece and Rome. Thus unemployment was conquered in an unscientific world.

Transportation in the days of the Ptolemies was not essentially different from that in the days of the Cæsars; while transportation at the close of the 18th century was little if any advanced over Roman methods.

By the opening of the 19th century a mighty revolution had come upon western Europe. The direct cause of this upheaval was the invention of the steam engine by James Watt in 1769. As precursors to this invention we note the rapid strides in metallurgy, as well also as skill in the rolling of sheet iron and in the machining of movable parts.

It was not long after the introduction of mechanical contrivances for pumping water from mines and especially in substitution of hand labor in the textile mills of England that we record the invention of the locomotive by Trevithick in 1804 but not translated into a steam-powered train on tracks until 1825 by Stephenson. The steamboat of Fulton, however, came into the picture as early as 1807 and the first crossing of the Atlantic was accomplished by the S.S. "Savannah" as early as 1819.

Thus the mechanical revolution had struck. A mighty cataclysm falling upon a more or less self-ordered and self-satisfied world. By one fell swoop the human drudge had become emancipated. Cheap human labor (the mainstay of ruling powers) had need to be exchanged for cheap mechanical power.

It is needless to describe the fears of those days. The people were decidedly antagonistic to all innovations of a mechanical nature. In London groups of citizens were constantly avenging themselves against such devilish devices by demolishing every machine that could be found. These groups of men foresaw a decrease in hand labor and hence in general employment. Their future was at stake and naturally they

THE CHEMICAL REVOLUTION

strove to destroy that which threatened to destroy the means of their livelihood.

In spite of all drawbacks scientific progress made steady headway. England soon came to be the center for machinery required in the making of tools. Increasing demands came from continental Europe and America. The mechanical arts were thus born in England. In the wake of this development arose increasing demands for labor; thus the earlier discontent among workmen against mechanical inventions slowly subsided. The great coal beds in the British Isles contributed in no small way to this centralization of manufacture in England. Low-priced coal and iron ore ensure low-priced machinery.

The advance from horse and man power to steam power worked havoc in the ancient methods of transportation. As the medieval period in history witnessed no particular advance in transportation or in the means of communication we naturally must draw our comparison directly with ancient peoples. The mechanical revolution served to foreshorten the correlation of time and distance. Individuals moved further from central sources of supply. Civilization was extended to distant frontiers. In this country the trek westward was supported by ever-extending railway lines until all sections of our western domain

THE FARM CHEMURGIC

became closely interlocked through a network of railways and served through eastern systems.

This spread of peoples to the outermost bounds of their physical domains obviated in the newly settled countries any particular rise in general unemployment, no matter from what cause. Temporary set-backs of course arose from time to time but these were the result more particularly of financial mismanagement. Over-production became apparent in the older and more densely populated districts of Europe but was slowly alleviated by emigration of the excess population to America.

The mechanical revolution brought man up to a newer and higher plane of living. The world at last began to show itself as an enlarged family circle. The great contribution of this revolution to mankind was the inauguration of our Industrial Era. This dates from 1856 with the invention of the Bessemer furnace for the production of steel. From that day on mass production and the introduction of replaceable units in manufacture have dominated all industry.

During the later years of the 19th century discoveries in the field of chemistry were reflecting the advances made just one hundred years earlier in the field of physics. In 1856 Sir William H. Perkin accidentally prepared a dye (called mauve) from aniline,

THE CHEMICAL REVOLUTION

a derivative of benzene which latter constitutes a lighter portion of coal-tar distillate. The commercial manufacture of mauve began at once. Up to this time no living man had any conception concerning the cause of color in nature.

Now the lure of color has ever existed in the human race. When we behold the gorgeous and variegated hues with which nature bedecks the lower forms of life, color seems unreasonably absent in man. Earlier savages smeared their bodies with certain metallic oxides of color, but as civilization dawned (synchronous with the rise of agriculture) recourse to juices of plants afforded a more abundant and simpler means for man's embellishment.

Though chemists directed their best efforts to solving the mysteries of nature these quests were none too rapidly rewarded. The primary cause of these earlier disappointments lay in the lack of a visual conception of the structure of the simplest types of organic chemical compounds. At last in 1865 Kekulé put forth his concept of the structural arrangement of carbon atoms in the benzene ring. This was the key that unlocked the door to a room of transcendent beauty in color and splendor. Attempt after attempt to build up by laboratory processes, *i.e.*, to synthesize, these beautiful and interesting compounds of nature met with triumph upon triumph and carried man into the heights of ecstasy. The synthesis of natural products by the investigator constitutes indeed the greatest exhilaration and contentment any mortal man can experience. Possibly in the world of artists it may be likened to the accomplishment of a beautiful and masterful symphony in color or sound.

Following mauve came the manufacture of several similar dyes, notably magenta and Hofmann's violet. These were not synthesized natural dyes; in fact they had no counterparts in nature. In 1868, however, Graebe and Liebermann in Germany discovered the constitution of alizarin, the dye of madder root and known particularly (with alumina as mordant) under the name of Turkey Red. This was the first of nature's dyes to be synthesized by man,—actually entering commercial production in 1869 both in England and Germany.

Prior to this time 70,000 tons of madder root were grown annually on the more than 400,000 acres devoted to its culture in Southern Europe. This output in pure alizarin came to 1,500,000 pounds valued at $15,000,000 ($10.00 per pound 100 per cent product). By 1878 there was under actual manufacture about 9,500 tons of 10 per cent alizarin paste (the equivalent of over 950,000 tons of madder root) with a monetary value of about $7,000,000,

THE CHEMICAL REVOLUTION

or about one-third the price it commanded upon an equality of tinctorial basis when supplied by nature. By 1895 Germany alone was exporting annually 9,000 tons of alizarin. The natural product was driven out forever.

Close upon synthetic alizarin came synthetic indigo —always termed "King of the dyes." This dye had been known from ancient times; it was cultivated extensively both in India and China, and to some extent in this country during early colonial days.

In 1897 synthetic indigo was placed on the market in Germany. Some 19 years of intensive research and expenditures covering millions of dollars had been required for the attainment of this much-coveted goal. Up to 1896 about 1,600,000 acres were under indigo cultivation with an annual yield of some 17,000,000 pounds of 65 per cent indigotine or color base valued at $20,000,000. By 1913, fifteen years after the commercial introduction of synthetic indigo, the acreage under indigo cultivation had dropped to under 200,000 but synthetic indigo had risen in production to over 13,000,000 pounds (100 per cent indigotine), valued at $10,000,000, thus selling at only about one-half the price of the natural product in 1896. By 1914 the price of indigo (20 per cent indigotine paste) delivered in New York was about 14.7 cents per pound. Today this price is more

THE FARM CHEMURGIC

or less stabilized, yet the production for world demands of 20 per cent paste has now risen to over 75,000,000 pounds. The victory of synthetic indigo was complete.

The story of synthetic indigo is to be likened to such vast engineering enterprises as was the building of a transcontinental railway system in this country. Years of grief and disappointment with millions upon millions of dollars seemingly dissipated; but in the end success and service.

Though the present indigo process was well established in laboratory by 1890, seven years elapsed before anything like commercialization of the preliminary manufacturing steps could be attained; these involved the manufacture on large scale of the reagents,——concentrated sulphuric acid, ammonia, acetic acid, metallic sodium, caustic soda, and chlorine, and steps for their recovery, to say nothing of benzene or naphthalene as starting point. Today we realize all industry would be sorely distressed and handicapped were it not for the efficient operation of these processes set in motion by the simple manufacture of indigo. In general, technological advance in organic chemical industry builds decidedly for a nation's progress and security.

Following the commercial manufacture of indigo there came into synthetic production a vast array of

THE CHEMICAL REVOLUTION

dyes of all types. The necessary starting points of these dyes lay in the simpler fractions of coal-tar distillate, and hence to a large extent these dyes have been dubbed "coal-tar" dyes. In the growth of the synthetic dye industry we witness the replacement of thousands of acres of land formerly under cultivation of dye-producing plants and hence likewise the displacement of much agricultural labor.

The introduction of synthetic silk-like fibre for natural fibre constituted the second great conquest by the organic chemist. As early as 1889 in France we may record the first successful attempts in this direction by Count Hilaire de Chardonnet. In 1905 Cross and Bevan in England introduced the viscose type of artificial silk, commonly called rayon. By 1910 at Markus Hook, New Jersey, our commercial production of viscose silk was under way. By 1926 our plants were producing 60,000,000 pounds of a then 200,000,000 pound output of the world's artificial silk. In 1931 we produced 144,000,000 pounds of the world's 480,000,000 pound output. In 1933 we manufactured 208,000,000 pounds of artificial silk made up of 76 per cent viscose silk, 17 per cent acetate silk and 7 per cent other types. The world's total output in 1933 was 650,000,000 pounds.

The basis of silk-like fibre is alpha cellulose. Cotton consists of 98 to 99 per cent pure alpha-cellulose.

THE FARM CHEMURGIC

When wood is used as the starting material, the lignin, pentosans, and hexosans, constituting about one-third of its weight, are removed in digesters and finally an alpha-cellulose of from 97 to 98 per cent purity is obtained. The cost of this latter is never over four cents per pound. Hence artificial silk-like fibre is based upon a price for alpha-cellulose which forever forbids cotton, in substitution thereof, to rise materially over about five cents per pound on our present-day dollar valuation. In other words, alpha-cellulose from cheaper sources spells the doom of cotton plantations except where cotton filament as such is demanded in the textile industry.

When alpha-cellulose is brought into solution in certain media by any one of several processes and precipitated therefrom again as alpha-cellulose fibre it is called regenerated cellulose, or, what is viscose or rayon silk-like fibre. When, however, alpha-cellulose (here preferably the purest obtainable such as cotton linters) is brought into reaction with acetic acid in dehydrated form this cotton becomes acetylated and from such solutions its precipitation in the form of cellulose acetate gives what is called acetate silk. At the present this acetate silk carries a cost almost twice that of rayon.

The replacement of cotton and woolen garments by cloth of silk-like fibre is proceeding at definite and

THE CHEMICAL REVOLUTION

assured rates. Eventually both cotton and wool will meet their Waterloo as far as finest cloth is concerned. Thus the land given over to the cultivation of cotton and eventually that to the grazing of sheep is slowly but surely passing out of the picture.

In 1909 Dr. Leo Baekeland in New York was able to bring about a condensation of phenol (the hydroxyl [OH] derivative of benzene) and formaldehyde to produce a resin capable of being moulded to the desired form under heat. This resin he called *Bakelite*. By 1910 a small commercial plant for its manufacture was in operation and by 1922 over 6,000,000 pounds of bakelite was being manufactured in the United States alone. By 1924 this quantity had doubled and by 1931 there was manufactured 34,000,000 pounds of all classes of these resins known now as synthetic plastics. The introduction of these synthetic plastics struck first at such natural products as amber, bone and horn. Then later as material of definite solubility was attained we came upon excellent substitutes for fossil gums, and shellac, used in varnishes. The net result here has not been so much the elimination of acreage from cultivation as it has been the elimination of cheaper labor devoted to the gathering of these natural resins and gums.

The next great chemical stroke was that of Fritz

THE FARM CHEMURGIC

Haber which, begun back in 1903, did not culminate until 1913, when the Haber-Bosch plant at Oppau, Germany, began production of synthetic ammonia from hydrogen and atmospheric nitrogen at the rate of about 7,000 tons annually.

This small plant made the World War possible. Without it and its enlargements there would have been no World War in 1914. By 1928 Germany's production of fixed nitrogen exceeded 400,000 tons per year which amount contains more fixed nitrogen than is to be found in the total annual export of sodium nitrate from Chile. Today Germany can produce 1,000,000 tons of fixed nitrogen annually and the rest of the world taken together can synthesize about the same quantity.

Here there was a real encroachment upon natural sources for the supply of nitrogen. The Haber-Bosch process, at first regarded only as of theoretical interest, later claimed attention as of basic value. Today, in the light of agricultural power, we know that this invention is to be regarded as of far greater significance in the history of the world than the steam engine itself.

The Haber-Bosch process gives to man unlimited command of explosives and fertilizer. Through it the naturally occurring nitrogenous fertilizers are rendered entirely superfluous. This process opened

THE CHEMICAL REVOLUTION

up the air to chemical exploitation, whereas Watt opened up steam to mechanical exploitation. In supply to the former, the earth's atmosphere holds 4,000 million million tons of nitrogen; in supply to the latter, the oceans alone contain 1,500 million million tons of water. The two inventions are exact counterparts,—the latter leads to mechanical adaptations, the former to chemical adaptations,—but through these we can produce all mechanical measures desired. Particularly does this reveal itself when we consider the production of carbohydrates and their fermentation into alcohol and the latter's use in internal combustion engines.

In dyes, artificial fibre, synthetic plastics and synthetic ammonia as well as the numerous lesser discoveries, the labor and habits of over 25 per cent of the population in Europe and America have been rendered futile. Humanity staggering under these distressing conditions lay prostrate, as it were, when suddenly a crash disturbed the setting. It was 1914; the world was face to face with war. Temporarily at least, war activities might direct men to new adventure. In other words, the urge to manufacture at all speed in order to destroy at whatsoever cost came as a hope of relief! We were as chemical imbeciles. The torches of chemical power had been thrust into our hands; we scampered about bent upon manufacture

THE FARM CHEMURGIC

and destruction. We destroyed even faster than we could replace. We awoke to find ourselves in a mighty whirl; a revolution affecting all mankind.

The great chemical revolution came upon us through the replacement of naturally grown chemical products by those of synthetic chemical manufacture. Millions of men upon millions of acres witnessed their means of livelihood pass out from under them. These acres, once under cultivation of strictly chemical products for other than food industries, received no attention by way of introduction of yet newer and more promising chemical flora. The farmers were left to drift. Naturally they had naught else but to cultivate their lands after the pristine practices of early peoples, namely for supply of food and raiment alone.

The blame for all of this falls directly upon the agricultural departments of the various governments. It would seem to be a part of their duty to study agriculture from all angles—the first angle is the chemical angle and the second is the biological. It so happens that nowadays all other angles receive more attention than these basic angles—and naturally agriculture suffers both here and elsewhere and will continue to suffer until the men in charge wake up to what chemi-biological requirements dictate.

THE CHEMICAL REVOLUTION

There is no blame falling on the farmer—it lies altogether on the government.

This great chemical revolution naturally had its roots far back in the preceding century,—as far back as the opening of the Industrial Era,—but chemically speaking the first appreciable replacement by man of nature's handiwork, such as in the replacement of natural madder root by its synthetic counterpart, alizarin, may be cited as its inception. The final blow that threw the world into chemical cataclysm was the Haber-Bosch process for synthetic ammonia. The year 1913, therefore, may be taken as the actual date when the revolution took effect.

The First Stage in the chemical revolution is of course the World War—1914 to 1918. This war accomplished nothing of note save to spread the knowledge of synthetic chemistry and its latent powers. It marks the rise of chemi-consciousness in the world. So great indeed is the stupidity of man that only by such frightful orgies can he be forced to embrace so great a scientific principle.

The Second Stage in this revolution is the period of Recuperation—1919 to 1923. Industry and agriculture were entirely out of line with daily life; hence ample time was required before proper readjustments could be made. Here was the proper time for scientists to have been called to the directorships of

THE FARM CHEMURGIC

all companies and to all governmental departments. This, of course, smacked too much of ratiocination and the war rulers of the world turned a deaf ear. Adjustments between industry and agriculture were totally neglected.

The Third Stage of this revolution is that of Phantom Prosperity—1924 to 1928. The great financial boobs, or so-called international bankers, and their coterie here gained the upper hand. Just how this came about little is known save that they seemingly possessed secrets whereby to increase our exports in industry and agriculture. Even though prior to this period we knew that our consumption and production were not in balance, still the average citizen had by now become mesmerized into accepting bonds of foreign countries to whom the boobs were loaning money in order that these foreign peoples could buy our surplus production. There may be elsewhere recorded somewhere in the march of man a like procedure of such diabolical import but history prefereth it kept dark.

The Fourth Stage of this revolution is of course the upheaval that had to follow in the wake of the Third Stage. We had learned well to manufacture under increased stress and naturally the world was being flooded with American goods. The inability of foreign countries to pay for these goods gradually

THE CHEMICAL REVOLUTION

became apparent and one country after another defaulted on its bonds. This meant that all we had manufactured and sent abroad was a gratuitous offering on the part of the American. This stage is called the Depression—or more aptly the Great Financial Debauch—1929 to 1932. Its close is that point at which securities were at lowest ebb and industry and agriculture left floundering in the slough of despond. Thus by the middle of 1932 the chemical revolution had terminated. Common sense once more gained the saddle and chemically man began to pick his way out of the morass.

The Fifth Stage of the chemical revolution, or aftermath of the revolution itself, is the 1933-1936 period which describes the Chemical Readjustment Stage. In this country it may be included in the expression, "The Roosevelt Recovery." Certainly it is no revolution. The revolution has come and gone. This is the stage when man must get his house in chemical order. He must arrange his manufacture upon a chemical basis and under chemical guidance. He must conduct his business upon chemical and physical and biological principles; especially under chemical and biological direction must each and every agriculturist hereafter follow his daily routine.

There is no turning back—to desert this chemical trend is just like the early 19th century cranks re-

THE FARM CHEMURGIC

turning to oxen. Fertilizer was the inevitable and early end of both crank and ox. We must interpret everything from a chemical viewpoint—as there is nothing that mortal man can do on this earth that is not chemical and biological. Why not face the facts and become intelligently aware of our true status? Under such vision we can go ahead. If we pout and shirk in our duties we too shall find the abattoirs a welcome relief and certainly our deserved resting place.

The chemical revolution has brought us face to face with a chemical world; customs and habits must accord with chemical interpretations. Chemical adaptations will continue to open broad vistas of entrancing research destined to revolutionize the whole of man's activities. As we learn to adjust the applications of these researches into this or that channel we shall direct the balance of endeavor between citizens in every walk of life. Never again need there arise any such upheaval as lately experienced; never again need there be a dearth of work when men everywhere are eager for work.

CHAPTER II

Intense Nationalism

THE rise of nationalism is always marked after a war. The World War was no exception. On the other hand, nationalistic tendencies are now seen to have outrun all previous records.

In the World War millions of soldiers of almost every nationality were thrown into the fray against Germany. The fate of any single nation against the Germanic forces would have been as wax before the sun. In armament and training the Germans acknowledged no superior and in chemical technology they surpassed the world.

Small wonder that the chemical prowess of Germany stamped itself so indelibly on the hearts and minds of combatants engaged during those four years of strife. Their return to homelands after the war has never dimmed this imprint of the might and power that some day would control the destiny of man. Whatever nation may fail to keep abreast of chemical advance is certainly destined to subordinate position in the family of nations.

The unlimited supply of nitrogen as diluent in

THE FARM CHEMURGIC

the atmosphere and its ease of "fixation" or combination into useful forms to serve mankind, has given us the most far-reaching of weapons. The first and most urgent application was in the manufacture of explosives,—nitrates and nitro-organic compounds, thus making each center engaging in such manufacture completely and for all time independent of any importation of mineral nitrates. The second and most important application was in the manufacture of fertilizers. Through ammonia and its derivatives, associated with proper admixtures of potash and phosphates, intensive cultivation of the land becomes productive of the most luxuriant yields in all agricultural staples. Furthermore, the carbonaceous residues from such crops offer abundant sources of supply for the organic constituents required in the manufacture of nitro-organic explosives above mentioned. Thus, in this one nitrogen fixation process lay the secret of any nation's complete military independence.

In lieu of the tremendous advantages possible to accrue to a country developing fixed nitrogen there arose among the nations of the world an urge to become more and more self-sufficient and to acquire a preparedness such that security against foreign attack might be guaranteed. The guarantee of any one nation's possessions by a more powerful neigh-

INTENSE NATIONALISM

bor is only another way of expressing the weakness of the former. Chemi-technological advance has only just begun. Not alone in the manufacture of explosives and fertilizers but likewise in all marketable goods do we note this growing enthusiasm. Naturally the basic products of largest tonnage claim first concern. Thus where sulphur need be imported into Germany we now find the Germans perfecting processes for extraction of sulphur from their own mineral sulphates. In Italy the preparation of elemental phosphorus from Italian phosphates affords a latent power magazine owing to the ease of storage of such phosphorus underground.

On February 14, 1918, and taking effect two days thereafter, President Wilson, under powers conferred upon him by the Trading with the Enemy Act of 1917, issued a proclamation amounting virtually to an embargo on various products including dyes and chemicals. This Act, with minor modifications, continued in force up to September 21, 1922, the date of passage of the Fordney-McCumber Tariff. The rapid strides in organic chemical manufacture during this period of four and one-half years led directly to generous protection in the 1922 Tariff Act.

It was given to President Wilson to visualize the position chemistry must hold in the life of every

THE FARM CHEMURGIC

modern nation; to realize the utter dependence of all manufacture upon chemical technology; and to urge the support of our government to all things chemical.

All that may be written in praise of the idealism of President Wilson is as by-play in the eyes of those who know and can realize the importance of the chemical industry in its bearings and relations with all industry and agriculture. In President Wilson's prophetic vision and insistence upon protection for the chemical industry of this country posterity will acknowledge indeed the highest contribution of this educator to the great American commonwealth. How remote this basic concept from the idealism for which and in which he lived and labored! Yet upon close analysis all these noble concepts that were his counted for naught over against the gigantic enterprise he set in motion through his chemical foresight. As Abraham Lincoln is known for the emancipation of the slave so shall Woodrow Wilson be known as the emancipator of American science and industry.

As we look back upon this eventful period in the building of our nation we cannot omit the mention of that fighting crusader who, impressed with a vision of the might and limitless power that lay within a chemical nation, feared not to combat and destroy all sinister influences at work within our domain, in order that this nation might attain chemical inde-

INTENSE NATIONALISM

pendence. Upon Francis P. Garvan fell the mantle of American Chemical Leadership. It was he who sensed the subservience of our nation to foreign scientific mastery; it was he who spread before President Wilson the utter necessity of curbing foreign domination over our enterprises; it was he who advocated the breaking asunder of all ties to foreign bondage.

In the Act of November 4, 1918, Congress passed a law authorizing the seizure of patents, trademarks, and the like, belonging to enemy countries. Following this came another Act of Congress authorizing the President to dispose of these patents to American citizens "at public auction, private sale, or otherwise." Shortly thereafter an executive order from the White House authorized the sale of these patents to the Chemical Foundation over which the President himself wisely designated that Francis P. Garvan be made president to serve without pay and without financial interest in the chemical companies involved.

Since those early days, Mr. Garvan, with unswerving purpose, has devoted his time and fortune to the advancement of chemical and allied science and industry in the United States. About him he has gathered men of learning and of courage, fearing neither man nor devil; these men have ever acted as constructionists in the building of our nation, realizing full well that the chemical independence of a

THE FARM CHEMURGIC

nation alone bespeaks true independence. How different the ideals and inspirations of these men in comparison with those of the destructionist type who would exert their baneful influence among presidential advisors of today. The future of a stalwart nation rests upon riddance of all destructionists from among its populace.

During the World War period this country definitely entered industrial status. In the automotive industry we recognize the prime factor that instituted our transformation from agricultural to industrial position. In its consummation we called for raw products from all sections of the country; interception in any one source of supply being readily compensated by other sections. In other words, this automotive industry had every assurance of a constant source of supply from within the nation,—save possibly for rubber,—and even this lately is fast coming under home control through synthetic duprene. Thus, it was not given to an outside agency to interfere with the development of our great automotive industry.

So likewise in our chemical development it becomes more and more necessary to rely exclusively upon home supply for basic raw chemicals. Before the War there was little or no chemical industry in the United States. Had we had no protection follow-

INTENSE NATIONALISM

ing the War for the basic organic chemical industry we should have no independence today in our chemical fields. There is here no debt of gratitude to be paid to a foreign country, as there exists no foreign country overly zealous for us to develop anything that they themselves already have developed. Hence the vast and extensive effect of the Fordney-McCumber Tariff of 1922 on all chemical enterprise in this country,—which of course signifies our industrial life itself.

We read now and then of the childish remarks of short-sighted industrial leaders who, impelled by greed, would seek further exports of their particular products no matter what the effect on other industries. Even automobile leaders are known to have proclaimed that we need less tariffs in the world so that we can sell more cars abroad. How many of these have the insight to comprehend the close relationship of their industry with the basic chemical industry! President Wilson, high in Democratic councils, needed no suggestions on this point. He knew, and so do all of us of advanced chemical training, that if the tariffs were removed on basic chemicals, the basic chemical industry would pass into the hands of foreign manufacturers and remain there. Soon the many distinct parts making up the automobile could be purchased more cheaply abroad and

THE FARM CHEMURGIC

then only a little while would elapse before the automobile itself would become the exclusive product of foreign manufacture.

Tariff walls in foreign countries are becoming ever stronger and stronger, or shall we say, higher and higher. This is exactly in accord with reason. Were there to be a lowering of these tariffs against foreign nations we might well accuse the rulers of such nations of madness. In other words, tariffs signify that at one and the same time there arises a determination and will power on the part of governments commensurate with latent resourcefulness on the part of their people. We are still looking for that industrialist who, dwelling within a country surrounded by tariff walls, would move himself and family to a country that offered no protection to its industries. Of course, the old-time British so-called "free-trade hoax" is here to be classified in its true light, namely, "embargo at will."

We cannot condone excessive tariff rates but it is not for us to judge another country in this respect. Eventually a sort of give and take policy will iron out the severe handicaps in international trade. There is, however, no hope in this direction for the United States so long as we talk of dumping our agricultural products on foreign markets.

As much as our theorists may deplore this tend-

INTENSE NATIONALISM

ency in tariff rise throughout the world we must realize that it is the aftermath of the World War and directly due to the spread of chemi-consciousness over all civilized nations. Wheresoever this tendency has asserted itself following previous wars it slowly weakened in the face of needed imports of raw chemical products. The Haber-Bosch process with consequent cheap fertilizer made almost universal the ready cultivation of farm crops all over the world and thus brought each nation into chemical power. Metaphorically speaking, the Haber-Bosch process opened the atmosphere to chemical use. From this, indirectly, we snatch the products of a world of nations. International trade fades into insignificance. National development becomes the ruling motif. Hence there can be no weakening now. And if, perchance, a weakening does arise in some country we shall see there the dismemberment of that country among her more powerful neighbors.

We picture, therefore, the rise and growth of the most intense nationalism conceivable by mortal man. This outgrowth of the chemical revolution is the greatest lesson of the revolution itself and simultaneously will constitute the undoing of every nation that does not grasp its precepts. It is not enough merely to acknowledge this guiding power; we must inculcate our every citizen with its teachings. We

THE FARM CHEMURGIC

must bring the common people up to an understanding of everything chemical. Scientific principles shall be taught in our elementary schools. History is replete with the fall of empires due primarily to withholding of education from the lower classes;—witness the fall of Rome. Today we are at the fork in the roads—the chemical road leads on to fortune but dissolution awaits the nation that travels the other road.

The underlying principle is simply stated: each and every man, at whatsoever spot on this earth, has abundant opportunity to feed, clothe, and house himself by chemical adaptation of the things about him. Any government that essays to limit these rights, through indirection or thwarting of his proper protection, by violating such laudable pursuit, is doomed to destruction. And blessed be the day that destruction comes to the unscientific! Any man or group of men who assail the rights of others to this self-containment shall be cursed forever.

As the coming of the mechanical revolution released human slavery so the goal of the chemical revolution is the freeing of national slavery. Throughout the ages man has suffered oppression at the hands of such as kings, feudal lords and church despots who counted ever on slavery as their power. Today all such power is rapidly dissipating. The

INTENSE NATIONALISM

scientifically managed government will prevail and kings, lords, and churchmen must cast their lot with scientific control.

We are entering the great era of Chemical Dominance. All material transformations on this earth must come under chemical study and guidance,—and that simply because there are no material things on this earth that are not made up of chemical elements and compounds. No more pertinent maxim could possibly be conceived. Our advance must be under careful chemical, physical, and biological supervision; otherwise no advance. Experimentation is of course commendable but by substantial results alone can we have any basis for progress.

There is an old-time doctrine of Adam Smith—that nations prosper through exchange of wealth. In olden days such interchange led to a spread of improvements and thus to allied inventions. Today by letter or even by telephone we ascertain every step of advance in every country and in a few hours someone has duplicated and improved this step. Give us a description of what you have and we will better what you can make,—we don't even need a picture of it. Thus exchange of goods between nations plays no particular rôle save to balance production among the several countries. As scientific management comes to the fore the internal balance in any one

THE FARM CHEMURGIC

country is more likely to be assured and consequently the country itself becomes more and more self-contained. Thus to speak of prosperity dependent upon the exchange of wealth between nations is an insult to a scientifically minded people.

It is this self-containment that is to make for power and grandeur. It is the goal all modern nations seek. Wherein it fails, that is, wherever dependence of a nation upon import is measurable, we note exactly to that same degree is this nation vulnerable to attack. It is here that the grouping of peoples of close ethnological traits will strengthen the resultant group for its own advancement. Such as, for example, that of Austria with Germany in the making of a stronger Germanic unit; childish jealousies among European nations for the present prevent this union. They cannot understand the chemical drift that necessitates powerful national units. In the end, of course, this union will take place and any nation striving by war to prevent the same will certainly dig its own grave.

The rise of intense nationalism characterizes our times. We may smile as we read of efforts here and there put forth by effete governments working toward temporary international conciliations,—just short-lived efforts to gain a little export trade. Nothing in the main will result save subservience of

INTENSE NATIONALISM

one nation to another. If in the end this is of advantage to a nation, all well and good; let us work with them. But never imagine a powerful nation will long permit such ignominy in the light of knowledge that so surely points the way and guarantees complete self-containment to all who will.

If we would become a power in highly diversified manufacture we must have a tariff of our own making,—no advice from without. Foreign nations are not in the habit of throwing anything our way save obstacles,—and yet we have pacifists or decadent mentalities still extant!

In intense nationalism, therefore, lies the hope of scientific nations. Whatever dominions may still choose to remain primarily agricultural shall constitute the hinterland, as it were, of civilization,—the barbarians as of old. They shall live in peace and contentment pending the day when the mightier nations will take over their lands for more intensive cultivation and development. These agricultural or peasant populations need have no tariffs as they have nothing to protect and in agricultural products their supply may well constitute the cheapest available organic chemical materials more and more needed by the scientifically operated powers.

CHAPTER III
Property Valuation

THE rise of nationalism the world over makes necessary a close scientific survey of all that functions within a nation's domain. It is well to know that production units are undergoing constant refinement so as best to meet new and keenest competition, and that all means of service are under the best of supervision.

Chemi-economic or chemeconomic considerations of national and international matters presage a standardization in some degree of monetary units. If a nation's currency must have a metallic backing then let us make it of the noblest and most useful of metals; the more noble a metal the more resistant to ordinary chemical action. Psychologically as well as chemically the human race has not as yet reached that enlightened state when metals are as slag and metallurgical processes command little or no pecuniary outlay.

It matters not that Aaron and his wandering tribes constructed for worship a dirty yellow calf of gold. This is no reason for placing a high value on so

PROPERTY VALUATION

brassy appearing metal. Chemically speaking, gold has little or no use,—hence no intrinsic value. The world might lose all its 600,000,000 ounces of stock gold overnight and in the morning no whimper of lament resound. Progress does not call for gold.

The noblest metals are silver-white. Platinum is such and possesses likewise many valuable attributes; it is far superior to gold as a metal. There are about 6,000,000 ounces of platinum on hand and the annual increase runs at about 200,000 ounces. Though much rarer than gold it carries not quite so high a dollar value per ounce; so greatly have we over-estimated (by 100 times) the value of gold! It would seem that the scarcity of platinum and the exceeding difficulty of its extraction from ores would recommend its worship on the part of internationalists in their diabolical desires to manipulate prices. Evidently we under-rate Aaronesque devotion.

Silver, a semi-noble metal of the class of gold, possesses widely extensive use. Without it photography and the moving picture would pass into second-rate position. There are about 12,000,000,000 ounces of silver on hand, hence of course it is cheaper than gold or platinum. Nevertheless it is widely distributed over the earth's surface and thus when brought into monetary service can serve the world as a whole. An alloy of platinum, silver and gold may well con-

THE FARM CHEMURGIC

stitute an ideal composition as metallic backing for international currency. Three metals, not necessarily alloyed, even better than two, add greater stability to a currency system.

Wherever a single rare metal, such as gold, is employed as monetary standard, there is constant danger that an increasing demand for it, instituted by financial uncertainties and by psychological frenzy, will force the price up beyond all reason, especially when the average annual increment of supply is failing. Today gold is valued at $35 an ounce; tomorrow it may well reach $100 an ounce. The average annual world increase in gold monetary stocks runs at about 3.15 per cent, but in recent years this increase has not been attained. In 1933, 24,720,000 ounces was mined but not all of this entered gold monetary stocks.

If there arises a much higher fictitious value for gold we may confidently look for its extraction direct from the sea. As chemistry and metallurgy advance we note a lowering in costs for extraction of elements from media in which they are more highly dispersed. Today 16,000 pounds of bromine is extracted daily from 300 million pounds of Atlantic Ocean in which bromine occurs 67 parts per million; and the cost of this pure bromine is no greater than where obtained from a brine of twenty times the bromine content of

PROPERTY VALUATION

the sea. Along with this bromine there passes through the Ethyl-Dow Chemical plant at Wilmington, North Carolina, 2.4 parts of gold per billion of sea water and about twice this portion of silver,—some $500 worth of gold per day. Its extraction is entirely possible, though for commercial purposes other sites are more likely to be chosen.

When once the chemist goes into the gold-extracting problem, look out! The gold bubble will be punctured and punctured a-plenty. There's only enough gold in the sea to make possible its distribution equally among all the inhabitants of this earth to the extent of one million dollars each! And this takes no account of its distribution on the land!

This is only another way of stating that if nations are going to insist childishly on gold as the only metallic standard then the chemist will soon be ready to wreck this standard. It is far safer to employ a group of metals in what has been termed a symmetallic base in order that the effect of fluctuations in value of each may be minimized.

When once a monetary base is established we are in position to estimate the value of property in general. It seems increasingly difficult for the state authorities to realize the chemical disintegration through which every edifice is daily passing. For tax and other purposes they are wont to look upon every-

THE FARM CHEMURGIC

thing built by man as eternal. This attitude of course is utter nonsense and inimical to the best interest of both state and nation.

On the other hand, the owner of tangible property is painfully aware of the crumbling nature of all man's handiwork. Much of his life indeed is spent in the repair and preservation of such handiwork even under the severest penalties. There can never be forward progress in the matter of property considerations until governmental authorities accede to valuation estimated in the hands of properly selected scientific men.

No man-made structure is worth more than its cost of construction, inclusive of reasonable profit. If marketable property brings a price above this total cost then some psychological influence or intangible asset has recorded itself in the final transaction. We assume of course that in the interim no change has occurred in the monetary standard. Furthermore, we cannot include here the unearned increment falling to land values within cities. This can be anything and properly belongs to the cities themselves as has been expounded in the writings of John Stuart Mill.

The conclusion above is forced upon us. Given any definite and non-variant undertaking by man, involving the employment of a definite number of workmen and a constant source of raw material, it is well

PROPERTY VALUATION

established that in the normal course of events there will be recorded an overall gain in efficiency of about 5 to 10 per cent per annum.

With high-class concerns the annual gain in efficiency mounts much more rapidly. In general manufacturing operations we observe about 10 per cent rise in efficiency per annum. This of course depicts actual improvements in a set task and cannot apply where changes in process or product are instituted; deviations at all times call for additional labor.

It is not difficult to understand nor sad to contemplate the steady annual elimination of labor. It spells human progress. Furthermore, in the study of a definite manufacturing enterprise, we note that the cost of finished product drops in pace with the drop in employees,—and saving in labor cost registers itself as the more appreciable portion of total saving. In other words, labor constitutes ever the largest single factor making up total cost in manufactured articles. Naturally, therefore, the greatest savings result through introduction of labor-saving devices. Hence the cry of the alarmists: "The machine is conquering man."

Now all estimated savings in costs are here based upon a monetary unit of metallic backing carrying a fixed value. If there were existent a monetary unit based upon many commodities, such as has been de-

THE FARM CHEMURGIC

scribed as a commodity dollar, this dollar value would likewise change from year to year as improvements in production of these commodities were recorded. The end result would be much smaller deviation year by year arising out of normal progress and improvements. In other words, the monetary unit and all handiwork of man would go hand in hand.

But as we have adhered to fictitious valuation of a single metal the actual lowering in cost price of an article renders the monetary unit capable of purchasing more of the article, *i.e.*, the metal value rises in relation to the commodity or article of manufacture. Those who labor get less of the metallic unit for their work.

The definite lowering in costs for all man-made structures, through scientific progress in general, is never properly registered in annual appraisements for such structures. Thus, steadily enhanced becomes the value in metallic unit currency out of all proportion to the ever-declining replacement value of structure. Within ten years or thereabouts such variance has mounted to over 50 per cent approximately of original value. If mortgages or liens on property have not been progressively lifted then the only adjustment is through a change in set value of monetary unit or

PROPERTY VALUATION

through financial panic. Usually the latter, but just recently both together.

In general, we must consider that the value of any ordinary structure approximates nil within 15 to 20 years. Even under constant attention mechanical units are of no value at the end of ten years; consequently we may assume that if proper amortization is made then the replacement costs and maintenance charges over the average amortization period constitute the entire valuation of any mechanical set-up. Machinery replacement costs today in our manufacturing industries call for more than one billion dollars annually. Five years ago this cost was a mere five million dollars.

Obsolescence likewise is creeping in upon all man's handiwork at frightful pace. Contributing largely to obsolescence, modern scientific discoveries are contracting ever shorter and shorter this time-period in which replacements absolutely must be made for any industry to keep abreast of the times. Particularly is this apparent in private residences and their equipment and most especially in pleasure vehicles as the automobile. In a modern world there can be no alternative to the statement: No handiwork of man from the day of its construction ever again reaches in value its original cost. Among savages, of course, we could not expect such principle to obtain.

39

THE FARM CHEMURGIC

When the citizens of state and nation are dealt with on a strictly scientific basis they will be found to coöperate in fullest degree toward the upbuilding of public domain. When these citizens are cowed into submission on whatever terms the political authorities may decide then the spirit of revolt will arise and insurrection cannot be far afield.

Our steady advance in manufacture with consequent release in employment at the rate of 5 to 10 per cent per year has recently arrested the attention of a group of statisticians. They foresaw the end of the industrial era and predicted dire calamity for the human race. Their contentions were not without merit. But they saw only one side of the picture, particularly because the real side was in eclipse by reason of the late phantom prosperity period.

It is here that research comes into its own and offers assured hope for all. During our early days as industrialists much of the research was directed into machinery and transportation units with the result that these products met a demand the world over. In the phantom prosperity period greedy bankers forced money out of its proper scientific channels and into speculations and foreign loans. There followed a tremendous retrenchment in proposed installations based on contemporary discovery and invention and in which previously our excess labor met ready em-

PROPERTY VALUATION

ployment. Then when exports fell off and home demands lessened there was scarcely anything new under way,—a complete paralysis of all industry.

The chemical industry, however, stood out apart. This industry took its rise during the World War and was well established within a few years after the 1922 Tariff Act. Research was prosecuted to the utter limit. Nothing daunted the entire industry. For the most part it escaped the clutches of damnable banking institutions of our large cities,—possibly because many types of chemical manufacture are not tolerated by city residents.

We can now record that the chemical industries weathered the depression period better than any other class of industry. They are continuously engaged in launching countless new enterprises. In number of employees today, these companies have long ago passed the peak of employment either in war or post-war periods. In other words, the chemical industries adhered strictly to scientific principles of which none is more fundamental than "constant change." Nothing is ever finished. Improvements every day in every way make life more chemical.

This fundamental chemeconomic principle that you must tear down what you construct in order to better construction and make room for improvements carries in its wake a most peculiar principle:

THE FARM CHEMURGIC

namely, to wit, that more and more skilled labor must be employed in the growth of any company so operating. That is, if a company essays the betterment of its own products there will be necessary annually to this end alone more skilled labor than is released annually by reason of actual manufacturing improvements.

So marked is this characteristic that its application to manufacturing organizations in general gives direct testimony revealing the true status of such organizations. The discharge of employees in itself is no criterion, as the less efficient always must give way to the skilled; but when more of the skilled are dropped than are taken on, then disintegration has begun.

It is here that we answer all alarmists. There is so much to be torn down and rebuilt in every walk of life that never can man satisfy man; never can the machine keep up with man.

In the outlays for research and investigation to be set aside by a corporation there must necessarily be a wide range. With the highest type of organization —particularly the chemical and electrical and food groups—the money expended upon research and development should reach an amount equivalent to 20 or 25 per cent of the net earnings of the company. Those banking institutions of the promoter or plun-

PROPERTY VALUATION

der type may not sanction such outlays but their influence is fast fading.

Following the panic of 1929 most of our manufacturing plants found themselves sorely pressed for financial credits. Research had need to be curtailed. By 1932 upwards of 13,000,000 citizens were out of work, yet of this number possibly 4,000,000 represented normal unemployment. During this period the value of all property sank to lowest level. Frantic foreigners were so intent upon withdrawing gold from this country that confidence among our own citizens was reaching the vanishing point.

Happily, President Franklin D. Roosevelt, on April 19, 1933, took this country off the gold standard and renounced once and for all the silly asinine gold clause contracts always insisted upon by Aaronesque officials. It was as if a modern Moses had come anew to overthrow the worshipers of the damnable yellow metal. This enabling act of Congress in the hands of President Roosevelt was the turning point of our day. Confidence swelled again in the human breast. The dire consequence of a one-metal monetary backing was fully realized. Ruin is its only reward. Happily we record that, by a recent Act of Congress, silver and gold together now constitute our present monetary standard.

CHAPTER IV

Property Taxation

PHYSICAL and chemical evaluation of man's handiwork offers the only rational basis for property taxation if property is to be taxed. We may view the chemical factor grown out of the physical just as the lessons of the chemical revolution are laid down upon those of the mechanical revolution.

No organization can afford to tear down its structures as soon as construction is completed. Yet this indeed is the action of an oxidizing atmosphere (the air) on all mundane things. Scientifically speaking, it may well become the duty of the state, if it would encourage industry and agriculture, to pay to the owners of real property certain sums with which these owners may keep the property in normal condition and thus insure to the state a maximum of revenues. This same end of course is better attainable by instilling within the citizenry an urge to better their own holdings.

Now this urge to improvement in properties can be obtained simply by the removal of all taxes. What one may do to improve his land or his home he then

PROPERTY TAXATION

will do with a freedom of spirit and for the beautification of his surroundings. Man should not be penalized for his good deeds; rather should he be encouraged to work with the state and for the good of the state. When we tax man for his good efforts he becomes as a whipped dog scowling at all officialdom. At this point, it is well for us to review briefly the history of this *bête noire* of modern civilization —the land and property tax.

The cities of ancient Greece did not tax land directly excepting in an emergency, yet in ancient Egypt and Babylon a definite land tax was assessed according to fertility of soil. Later the Romans, between 400 B.C. and 167 B.C. assessed a land tax to finance wars; but such taxes were returned if the wars proved successful. Following 167 B.C. imperial revenues enabled the Romans to dispense with any general system of direct taxation in the home province until the time of Diocletian. Thus from the time of the Ptolemies and other rulers of ancient peoples irregular methods of taxation burdened the civilized world.

In about 300 A.D. Diocletian introduced uniform rules governing methods of taxation for the Empire. These rules abolished the old intricate methods. In their place arose an oppressive system founded on exacting fixed contributions of produce and labor,

THE FARM CHEMURGIC

based on acreage. The marked exception throughout the ages was that in vogue in ancient Palestine. The Hebrews had evolved the only equitable policy—that of the tithe system. Its defects lay in its cumbersome methods of collection and in temptation to graft. In this tithe system we have the inception of our modern excise tax, or tax at source of production.

Following the Diocletian edicts, resistance has never abated toward oppressive methods of taxation. In addition to land and home taxes, we note the rise of tax on incomes as instituted in England in 1798. Other sources for revenue have been exploited from time to time till today we are face to face with the worst assortment of hodgepodge of debasing taxes the world has ever known.

All peoples have submitted more or less willingly to a certain degree of taxation, possibly because of the universal acceptance of the famous canon of Adam Smith in 1776. "The subjects of a state should contribute to the support of the government in proportion to their respective abilities." It would appear that the income tax more closely couples a reasonable degree of equality together with an ability to pay, but there are grave defects in the application of this tax.

About the middle of the eighteenth century in France a school known as the Physiocrats introduced

PROPERTY TAXATION

and advocated a "single tax" plan—a tax on rent of land. This was popularized by Henry George in 1879 when he recommended abolition of all taxes on industry and its products. Taxes were to be assessed against land values irrespective of improvements, and the difference in productivity between the worst and the best land was of course to give a direct means of affixing rent. The land belonged to the state.

About the middle of the nineteenth century John Stuart Mill urged the appropriation by the state of future "unearned increment" on land. The advance of land in agricultural value arises from "the improved skill, and knowledge, and exertion of the tenants, not the landlords." Adolph Wagner, in Germany, advocated private ownership of land but ownership of city land by the government, thus bringing into the public treasury all future increments in value. Many European countries have exempted from taxation for a period of years all improvements in properties. Today in France property that yields no income is temporarily removed from taxation.

It will be noted that these writers and many others of the eighteenth and nineteenth centuries were primarily philosophers. The political economy of those days took its foundation in philosophical concepts. Mill studied both physical and natural sciences and especially botany but in no sense did he study man

THE FARM CHEMURGIC

from a biological point of view. To all of them land was just land; and naturally so, as only by the close of the nineteenth century could anything definite be stated as to the chemical reactions activated within the living plant or animal.

In early days when little else beside tangible property carried any significance in gauging the wealth or affluence of man, it was natural that government authorities observed here the only point for affixing a tax that offered anything approaching continuity of existence or promised anything like an assuredness of income. The fertility of any section of land or the substantiality of buildings was taken as a mark of the order of wealth of those in possession thereof. It distinctly characterizes a period antedating chemical dominance.

The recent trend of higher and higher expenditures under government direction entailed, of course, a corresponding rise in taxes to be assessed against all sources of revenue. Though the point of "diminishing returns" as regards farm lands has long been passed, nevertheless, the old practice of placing a fine on the farmer—that is, a land tax—is strictly followed.

When overproduction is apparent, that is, in a market of falling prices, our obsolete system of taxation operates at its worst. It impedes any readjust-

PROPERTY TAXATION

ment or realignment between the factory or farm on the one hand and the open market on the other. Were our monetary system based upon a commodity dollar, for example, this disparity would have a tendency to disappear; but based, as it has been, upon a single metal standard, there is no possible way of meeting debts, save by continued overproduction. In other words, our static monetary system accentuates the very distress which the people would remedy.

Under present conditions it becomes necessary for each and every farmer, who would meet his tax assessments, to grow more and more of farm produce as prices on said produce drop in value in the open market; otherwise the farmer will fall into arrears and possibly be forced from his possessions by the foreclosure of a mortgage. It matters not whether the cost of producing his commodities exceeds the selling price—that is not a concern to one who would pay his fines. When a man is stalled in an automobile on a railway track he does not calculate the hourly return upon his efforts if by any amount of labor he can eventually remove himself from the track.

The accursed real estate taxes are primarily responsible for the distressed state of mankind today. We decry surplus and yet we do everything possible

THE FARM CHEMURGIC

to make surplus production a necessity. During the World War, and the period immediately following, there was opened up an unusually large foreign market especially for the products of our land. Following the World War, and as a consequence thereof, we find that the spread of chemi-consciousness throughout the world made it scientifically necessary on the part of other nations to import less and less of our products. This is exactly as was predicted by chemists. True, we still supply a considerable portion of the world's cotton, but this cannot long obtain in the light of what other nations are doing. These other peoples are not unintelligent; consequently they will improve themselves by chemically operating in the correct manner to their entire self-containment.

During the period of phantom prosperity our governmental commitments advanced out of all proportion to national earnings. When signs indicated falling prices and diminishing income throughout the nation, there was no effort on the part of federal or state governments to reduce expenditures. The result was a total collapse,—the greatest financial debacle of all times, 1929-1932.

As personal incomes dropped, taxes and other fixed assessments took on a frightful mien. Much, of course, could not and never will be collected. Improvements in buildings went by the board. Improve-

PROPERTY TAXATION

ments on the land were left to Fate. Fertilizers, so necessary to the replenishment of the soil and to the growth of higher quality of staples, have been totally neglected. The general urge has been to cut all costs, no matter what the outcome.

Our farms have been drained to the last drop of plant food in order that the tax collectors may be satiated and the mortgage holders appeased. It stands to reason that farm lands have deteriorated in large measure, possibly 50 per cent below their condition in 1929. If land taxes are long continued, we should expect another drop by 50 per cent within three or four years.

Now the measure of prosperity is in the velocity of turnover. The more often we can reinvest the proceeds from an enterprise, the more business we create and naturally the greater benefits accrue to the individual and to the state. Therefore, in keeping with such premise, it becomes the duty of the state to collect its revenues from the avenues of trade.

The manufacturers' excise tax, collected at point of origin, offers an ideal means of securing revenue from a going concern. Such taxes must be within reasonable limits and so small as not to constitute an undue burden upon consumer.

The sales tax represents the cut at the consumer's end. It is likewise easy of collection. It offers the

THE FARM CHEMURGIC

great advantage of a constant yielding revenue. No form of taxation can be simpler than the sales tax and none more just and equitable to the citizen. If there is any fear of hereby overtaxing the man who can scarcely secure his livelihood, then all plain foods and clothing should be excluded from tax lists.

Regulatory of such imposts made directly upon trade, especial guard must be placed on expenditures possible in the hands of the Government. Possibly 10 per cent of the annual income of a state may constitute the upper limit. If the total income reported by agriculture, industry, and various sources within a state, amounts to $300,000,000 and the total taxes collected by this state amount to $40,000,000, then the budget for all expenditures would not exceed $30,000,000. The surplus, or $10,000,000, may be conserved against years of lower tax returns. On such scheme the sales and excise taxes become god-sends to humanity. Public extravagances are eliminated.

Land by itself has little value. It is primarily the microscopic life and organic matter within the soil and the particular colloidal condition of the latter that constitutes the factors of value. Upon this physical status all soil displays its manufacturing assets in ammonia, carbon dioxide and water supply. These three compounds, free to all, are contributors not

PROPERTY TAXATION

alone to the compositions of all living matter but likewise are the gauge of the soil's productivity.

In short, one piece of soil is just about as valuable as any other piece in the same latitude, if ammonia, carbon dioxide and water supply are equal. Of course, the various types of soil are considered in direct comparison. Some day we shall modify even these types at will and in whatever direction desired.

Today we are at the third chemical stage in agriculture; that is, we are about to enter the water-control period. The organic-matter control has been in progress for many, many years. The inorganic-control period took its rise in the work of Liebig back in 1840. The fertilizer industry has followed his precepts. Had Henry George understood the complete dependence of agriculture upon ammonia, carbon dioxide and water, he never would have sponsored the plan of basing all taxes on land, a thing in itself almost without value. Be these things as every scientist knows, our Government authorities still follow in the footsteps of ancient peoples, knowing full well that nation after nation has vanished simply by reason of excessive tax burdens upon its own citizenry.

Upon careful study it will be seen that a land tax does not permit of long-time adjustments and chemical improvements within the soil itself. Rather does

THE FARM CHEMURGIC

it force the owner to drive production forward at all hazards. If we affix the tax upon those chemical transformations measured by actual output, then we do not penalize the farmer who would improve his installation.

In widely separate communities we observe already certain tax exemptions on property carrying a value under $3,000. Florida will vote this fall on an exemption of all homestead property valued under $5,000. This is a wonderful step forward. Furthermore, several states exempt taxes for state purposes only, but this is not enough. That state which exempts all realty from tax of any kind will be the leading state of the Union in the great era of chemical dominance now upon us.

Those who fail to grasp the chemical significance of tax exemption on realty will do well to ponder just what the farmer actually does. He is merely an assistant to nature in synthesizing carbohydrates, fats, and proteins. Nothing else can he do. In industry, too, the manufacturer is engaged only in chemical manipulations; be it wood products or fibre from cellulosic material grown on the farm, or metal products from ores collected in mines. If you want a truly basic tax, tax these chemical transformations and the world lies at your feet. But don't tax what inherently has no value.

PROPERTY TAXATION

Of what value is a manufacturing plant? Just a mass of brick, lumber, and glass filled with combustible material and metallic set-ups. Within ten years everything in and out of the place is scarcely worth carting away. To tax this junk is just as pointless as taxing land.

Without a tax, we shall permit the manufacturer to amortize his factory in shortest time and then install rapidly all available improvements. This will make for happier workmen operating under carefully controlled and hygienic conditions. Furthermore, overproduction will be most unlikely where an excise tax is made to apply.

The absence of a realty tax cannot be allowed to operate toward creating a nuisance. In each community certain regulations will operate to maintain definite standards. These standards will improve with the years. Within corporation limits of our cities there will need be assessed some small tax for protection against fire, burglary and the like. However, following the amortization period permitted for any structure, there will then need to be affixed some nuisance tax which, for instance, will double every few years. It won't be long before the old are replaced by strictly modern structures.

True, an enormous amount of work will be directed constantly toward the tearing down and re-

THE FARM CHEMURGIC

building of property. This will mark the next active period in our civilization. The Hottentots at the lower extreme have little urge for such changes— one hut may serve a generation or two. Between 60 and 65 per cent of the families in this country live in ramshackle homes that belie description; and half of these firetrap structures are far inferior to the great majority of barns occupied by the best of our cow population.

Let us not deceive ourselves. Civilization is at the crossroads. We may belittle communistic uprisings and cry down anarchistic signs, but this will avail us naught when once the populace is minded to throw out an oppressive officialdom.

Short-sighted and greedy interests must succumb. The spirit of coöperation shall prevail. In the coming of excise and sales taxes, coupled with income taxes in higher brackets, ample means for all revenue is afforded. Thus may be banished the detestable realty tax. It is contrary to the rights of free citizens and thwarts every urge in right-thinking men to cherish and improve that which they have labored to construct. It makes for slums, derelicts, and graft; and awakened people will tolerate it no more.

CHAPTER V

The Four Horsemen

THE universe as we know it is made up of the compounds of some ninety-two elements, as disstinctive forms of matter, together with many of these elements themselves in the free state. The smallest unit in which an element can exist and still display its definite characteristics is called an atom. This atomic theory had its inception in the writings of the Greek philosopher, Democritus, but was not established till the time of Dalton in England in 1808. When these atoms of the elements are united in definite proportions either with their own kind or with other atoms the resultant "molecular" structure is called a compound.

Thales, the first of Greek philosophers, assumed that *water* was the basic principle of all matter; Anaximander chose as basic principle something on the order of *earth;* Anaximenes believed that *air* was the embodiment of this principle; and Heraclitus propounded yet another principle in *fire*. Such were the early attempts to account for variety among earthly objects by metamorphosis within a single material cause. Empedocles adopted these four principles as the ultimate roots or "elements" of matter; and on these same "elements" Aristotle, in the fourth century B.C., built up his philosophy of material things. These "elements" were looked upon as embodying the fundamental properties of matter and variation in combinations between them was viewed as giving rise to the vast multitude of distinctive earthly substances. "Earth" was representative of cold and dryness; "Air" was representative of heat and wetness; "Water" was representative of cold and wetness; and "Fire" was representative of heat and dryness.

Beyond these "elements" Aristotle proposed a "primordial element" called "essence" (later to be called quintessence) and out of which the four earthly "elements" themselves were evolved.

Following the Greek philosophers an era of actual experimentation was developed by the Egyptians and by their successors, the Arabians. Through the latter and the Moors chemistry was preserved in alchemical cults till the day of its second entrance into Europe by way of Spain. The clear-thinking Western European succeeded in establishing the science upon a firm foundation. In 1661, Robert Boyle actually made the first distinction between element, compound, and mixture; with the result that chemical

THE FOUR HORSEMEN

elements, as we know them today, were soon under isolation from their naturally occurring minerals. The Aristotelian elements soon lost significance.

Those compounds produced by living organisms had somehow been held aloof from inert or non-living matter; the idea of a vital force distinguished the former. Then in 1828 Friedrich Woehler in Germany actually synthesized urea, a product of animal metabolism, from the elements carbon (C), hydrogen (H), oxygen (O), and nitrogen (N) as contained in one of these inert chemical compounds. No product of a living cell had ever before been made from inert matter. The first step in breaking down artificial distinctions between chemical compounds was accomplished. Hereby organic chemistry came to the fore and henceforth was made to embrace "the chemistry of the carbon compounds." Inorganic chemistry remained the chemistry of the other elements and their compounds.

Agriculture as a science concerns itself primarily with organic chemistry and springs almost wholly from the air. Though a great number of mineral ingredients contribute to the growth and structure of plants and animals they constitute only a few per cent of the total weight of all living things. These inorganic salts make their way into plant life through the roots. It becomes necessary, therefore, in the

THE FARM CHEMURGIC

study of life processes that we study the chemical agencies operating to build up the simplest of compounds found in living cells.

Now the basic organic compound occurring within living plant cells owes its origin to the reduction of carbon dioxide (CO_2) in the presence of water (H_2O). An energy source to this accomplishment is, of course, necessary and is supplied by sunlight. The medium or locale supplying the mineral salts and other agents is the soil.

In 1779 Ingen-Housz, a Dutch physician, discovered that the green leaves of a plant in sunlight absorb carbon dioxide from the air and simultaneously give up oxygen, but that the entire plant is always chemically operating to take up oxygen and give off carbon dioxide; this latter is its respiration. The first process is a chemical synthesis as it contributes to the building up of plant substance. It operates more speedily under sunlight, particularly those rays at the red end of the spectrum. Thus the growth of plant arises from predominance of the first reaction over the second, that is, synthesis under light (photosynthesis) over respiration.

In expressing this equilibrium chemically it is of course understood that carbon and oxygen are represented by the symbols C and O respectively, and that the proportion of these several atoms in one mole-

THE FOUR HORSEMEN

cule or unit of carbon dioxide produced by total combustion of carbon in oxygen or air points to the formula CO_2 for such compound. Water, the product of complete combustion of hydrogen in oxygen, possesses, of course, the well-known formula H_2O, and oxygen itself in molecular state is given the formula O_2. The equilibrium, therefore, is expressed as follows:

(Photosynthesis in sunlight)
$$CO_2 + H_2O \rightleftarrows O_2 + \text{Organic matter}$$
(Respiration in light and dark)

The green parts of a growing plant constitute the chemical factory of the vegetable world. It is here that two pigments, chlorophyll-a (blue-green) and chlorophyll-b (yellow-green), are located. These pigments are highly complex organic nuclei containing carbon, hydrogen, oxygen and nitrogen and magnesium; the atom of the inorganic element magnesium within the complex is linked to several nitrogen atoms each one of which is a constituent part of what is known as a pyrrole ring and of which the chlorophyll complex contains at least four.

The two types of chlorophyll occur in the plant along with several yellow pigments notably the carotinoids,—carotin and xanthophyll. All of these agents are scattered throughout the leaves in numerous structures called chloroplasts; many of these

THE FARM CHEMURGIC

chloroplasts may occur within a single plant cell and in fact they may be likened to the units of a chemical factory.

Carbon dioxide and water enter the plant chiefly through microscopic openings in the leaves called stomata; openings carefully protected by valves so as to limit the intake of these ingredients. When the sun shines the inhaled carbon dioxide and water come into reaction with chlorophyll-a at the magnesium position of its molecule and immediately the reduction of *carbonic acid,* $_{HO}^{HO}\!\!>\!C\!:\!O$ (representing the combination of carbon dioxide and water) is brought about to yield *formaldehyde* $_{H}^{H}\!\!>\!C\!:\!O$, which latter is simply carbonic acid in which an oxygen atom has been abstracted from each of its two hydroxyl (HO) groups. The magnesium atom in chlorophyll-a possesses that particular property of being able to hold in loose combination a molecule of carbonic acid. When the carbonic acid is reduced to formaldehyde the oxygen hereby liberated is taken up by the chlorophyll-a to yield chlorophyll-b and at the same time the magnesium atom is released fom its loose combination with a carbon-oxygen complex.

The structure of chlorophyll, as established by Richard Willstaetter and his co-workers in Germany, points to the formula $C_{55}H_{70}O_6N_4M_g$ for

THE FOUR HORSEMEN

chlorophyll-b and a less oxygen containing formula $C_{55}H_{72}O_5N_4Mg$ for chlorophyll-a. The molecular formulæ of carotin ($C_{40}H_{56}$) and of xanthophyll ($C_{40}H_{56}O_2$) differ only by two atoms of oxygen. It is supposed therefore that the function of the carotin is to reduce chlorophyll-b back into chlorophyll-a and thus itself be transformed into xanthophyll which in turn is capable of reduction back into carotin simply by agency of plant enzymes. The regeneration of chlorophyll-a by this procedure opens up again the processing of carbonic acid into formaldehyde as described above.

Within the chloroplasts there is thus accumulating more and more of the carbon-oxygen complex known as formaldehyde. This product possesses exceedingly active properties with a marked tendency to condense with itself. That form of condensation here concerned leads directly to the simple sugars. By such condensation three molecules of formaldehyde, $_H^H{>}C{:}O$, build up a chain of three carbon atoms as in $CH_2OH \cdot CHOH \cdot CHO$ (called glycerose) or in $CH_2OH \cdot CO \cdot CH_2OH$ (called dihydroxy acetone). Both of these compounds are sweet to the taste and may be regarded as the first distinct sugars.

Next in order two molecules of glycerose may condense to yield one molecule of *glucose* (simple

THE FARM CHEMURGIC

grape sugar) which possesses six carbon atoms in the molecule ($C_6H_{12}O_6$) or

($CH_2OH.CHOH.CHOH.CHOH.CHOH.CHO$);

or, on the other hand, one molecule of glycerose may condense with a molecule of dihydroxy acetone to yield one molecule of *fructose* (levulose) of the same empirical but different structural formula as glucose ($C_6H_{12}O_6$) or

($CH_2OH.CHOH.CHOH.CHOH.CO.CH_2OH$).

Though these two basic sugars are shown here in chain formulæ they actually exist primarily in ring structure. Finally the molecular union of a type of fructose with one of glucose leads to the higher sugar saccharose or *sucrose* (ordinary cane or beet sugar) with the empirical formula of $C_{12}H_{22}O_{11}$.

The six carbon sugars constitute the greater portion of our plant sugars. When formed in the plant they are transplanted (translocation) to all parts to serve in respiration, and, after simple extraction of a molecule of water between two molecules of simple sugar, to yield a slightly dehydrated but insoluble product for storage; that product formed from fructose is called *inulin* and that from glucose is called *starch*. Finally also for growth itself these slightly dehydrated forms can be converted into *cellulose* which constitutes the stem substance of plant cellular structure.

THE FOUR HORSEMEN

Sugars, starch, and cellulose in general comprise a great class of organic compounds known as *carbohydrates;* they are the direct result of photosyntheses in the plant world. These compounds are so named by reason of their chemical composition, consisting exclusively of carbon and that proportion of hydrogen and oxygen as occurs in the molecule of water,—that is, two parts hydrogen to one part oxygen. Thus the simplest carbohydrate is formaldehyde, H_2CO $(C + H_2O)$, wherein only one atom of carbon is associated with that amount of hydrogen and oxygen found in only one molecule of water. The formula for cellulose and starch is $(C_6H_{10}O_5)n$ where n represents the number of six carbon units in the aggregate,—a molecule of very high molecular weight.

The chemical reactions attending carbohydrate synthesis and decomposition within the cells of living plants are many and diverse. Suffice it to say that reduction and oxidation may proceed conjointly in the same molecule. For example, the hydroxyl group at one end of a simple type of sugar molecule may be deprived of its oxygen (reduced) while at the other end a hydrogen group may be made to take up oxygen (oxidized). An illustration of this is the conversion of the three-carbon sugar glycerose into lactic acid:—

THE FARM CHEMURGIC

$$CH_2OH \cdot CHOH \cdot CHO \to CH_3 \cdot CHOH \cdot COOH$$
(Glycerose) $\left(\begin{array}{c}\text{Reduced at left end}\\ \text{Oxidized at right end}\end{array}\right)$ → (Lactic acid)

Such chemical change is now known to be the effect of muscular exercise in the animal world, where glycogen (a carbohydrate more rapidly capable than starch of entering colloidal solution with water) is stored in the liver and muscle tissues. During exercise the glycogen is broken down into glucose and into lactic acid,—the latter possibly by way of glycerose as shown above.

The presence of the carboxyl group (–COOH) in an organic compound denotes an acid; that of a simple hydroxyl group denotes an alcohol,—the counterpart of a base in the inorganic world. Now the primary class of compounds in organic chemistry, is made up of carbon and hydrogen only,—these are called *hydrocarbons*. In this class methane (CH_4) is the simplest member; and the simplest alcohol therefore becomes methanol or wood alcohol or *methyl alcohol* (CH_3OH) wherein one hydrogen atom of methane is replaced by hydroxyl. The next alcohol in this series springs from a two-carbon chain hydrocarbon known as ethane ($CH_3 \cdot CH_3$ or C_2H_6). Its mono-hydroxyl derivative is $CH_3 \cdot CH_2OH$ or C_2H_5OH or *ethyl alcohol* (grain alcohol). The oxidation of this group, $-CH_2OH$, leads directly to

THE FOUR HORSEMEN

an aldehyde (–CHO) and then an acid (–COOH) as previously mentioned.

When now we form salts between organic acids and organic bases (alcohols) we come to what are called esters; and when acids of longer chains of carbons are concerned primarily with that reduced form of glycerose known as glycerol (CH$_2$OH . CHOH . CH$_2$OH) and commonly called glycerine, we have the *oils* and *fats*. These longer chain acids (usually of 12 to 18 carbon atoms) may be looked upon as originating through complete reduction of hydroxyl substituents in parent sugars, or more particularly by extended condensations involving acetaldehyde (CH$_3$. CHO)—the enzymatic oxidation product of lactic acid.

The whole process is described generically as *degradation*. It is through degradation steps, therefore, that our sugar, starch, inulin and cellulose give rise to oils and fats and other products on down to carbon dioxide and water.

In nature the glyceryl esters of fatty acids cover a wide range of combinations. Typical of a simple type is that of *tripalmitin,* a well-known fat occurring chiefly in palm oil and to some extent in lard. The structural formula is given below and is indicative of three molecules of palmitic acid (C$_{15}$H$_{31}$. COOH) esterified by one molecule of glycerol:—

THE FARM CHEMURGIC

CH$_2$.O.CO.CH$_2$.CH$_2$.CH$_2$.CH$_2$.CH$_2$.CH$_2$.CH$_2$.CH$_2$.CH$_2$.CH$_2$.CH$_2$.CH$_2$.CH$_2$.CH$_3$
CH.O.CO.CH$_2$.CH$_2$.CH$_2$.CH$_2$.CH$_2$.CH$_2$.CH$_2$.CH$_2$.CH$_2$.CH$_2$.CH$_2$.CH$_2$.CH$_2$.CH$_3$
CH$_2$.O.CO.CH$_2$.CH$_2$.CH$_2$.CH$_2$.CH$_2$.CH$_2$.CH$_2$.CH$_2$.CH$_2$.CH$_2$.CH$_2$.CH$_2$.CH$_2$.CH$_3$

We must next include the element nitrogen in life processes. This element comprises about four-fifths of our atmosphere. In combination with hydrogen as ammonia, (NH$_3$), it constitutes the chief nitrogen end-product in degradation of nitrogenous organic compounds. Nitrogen enters into life processes primarily through the nitrogen-hydrogen complex or amino group (–NH$_2$). The condensation of amino compounds with various intermediate stages of carbohydrate synthesis and degradation leads to more highly involved amino products, especially to those substances that polymerize (build up simple molecular units into large aggregate molecules) into compounds of high molecular weight. These latter comprise chiefly the *plant proteins*. When plant proteins are broken down in digestion processes within the animal a goodly portion of this hydrolized material is taken up in the blood stream and transported to various parts for further synthesis into *animal protein*.

The milk cow is thus seen to be a degrading machine for the conversion of cellulose (grass) and such into an aqueous emulsion of fats, sugar, and proteins, and a trace of mineral salts,—called milk.

THE FOUR HORSEMEN

Of course the grasses are nothing but moist air, *i.e.* carbon dioxide and water and a little nitrogen photosynthesized into carbohydrates and plant proteins together with traces of mineral salts. In the near future we shall be able to carry out these degradation steps without service of the cow. In other words these same enzymatic changes effective on cellulose in the cow's stomach and through the mammary glands will be capable of accomplishment in the chemists's reaction vessels.

Now the growth of a plant is dependent upon a great number of factors. Naturally the rate of growth must necessarily depend upon the speed of formaldehyde synthesis. This in turn must depend upon the concentration of carbon dioxide and water in contact with the leaf. Then again much depends upon the wave length and intensity of light falling on the plant, and yet again upon the temperature of surrounding media,—here preferably 25 to 35 degrees Centigrade.

An ordinary plant per square millimeter of leaf surface, has several hundred stomata supplying several hundred thousand chloroplasts in active service. In a sunflower leaf of some 30 square inches of surface it is calculated that there are about 12,000,000 stomata and 10,000,000,000 chloroplasts which in their photochemical syntheses within

THE FARM CHEMURGIC

just one hour of direct sunlight may absorb and chemically transform into plant food and structure two to three cubic inches of carbon dioxide; and with each molecule of carbon dioxide there is ever necessary a molecule of water to accompany same in its travels through the vegetable world. Of the two million million tons of carbon dioxide in the atmosphere not over one-fiftieth is taken up annually into the structure of living plants; and no account is taken here of carbon dioxide in the oceans which hold 20 to 25 times the quantity in the air.

The tremendous quantity of energy issuing from the sun staggers the imagination, but only a small fraction of one per cent of it ever reaches the earth. It is calculated that in the temperate zone about 500 calories per square centimeter is received on the earth's surface per day (1.5 calories per minute on cloudless days); much of the energy of course is reflected from the upper atmospheric envelope.

Upon each acre of soil, during a growing season of three months, we may assume that there is received direct from the sun an equivalent of energy equal to the heat produced in burning 250 tons of high carbon coal. Yet from the crops that ordinarily are raised on this acre of ground we can only secure a total in heat energy scarcely equal to the burning of one-third ton of coal. This means that during the

THE FOUR HORSEMEN

growing season we are utilizing only about one-tenth of one per cent of the solar energy falling on this particular area of the earth's surface. In the case of rapidly growing wood this quantity is more than doubled during the same growing season. Truly much of the sun's energy falling upon the surface of the earth is dissipated. It must not, however, be forgotten that considerable energy is required in the evaporation of water from surface of plant leaves in order to maintain circulation within plant itself; possibly the equivalent of 30 or 40 times that amount of energy represented by the combustion of the plant or at least 50 per cent of the total energy absorbed by the leaf. In fact it is well established that in the production of one pound of plant substance there must have been evaporated from the leaves of such plant about 350 pounds of water during this growth.

The energy required for translocation processes within the plant comes directly through oxidation of carbohydrates or those products of the first steps in photosyntheses from carbon dioxide and water. Such respiration on the part of the plant again supplies carbon dioxide and water to the air.

Of the inorganic ingredients in the soil we need mention salts of the metals potassium, magnesium, iron, and calcium and of the non-metals nitrogen,

THE FARM CHEMURGIC

phosphorus, sulphur, and silicon as of chief significance; even traces of other elements such as iodine and manganese have recently been found necessary.

In addition to mineral salts we find in the soil a vast host of micro-organisms destined to play an essential rôle in plant growth. These organisms are of one-celled structure. That class known as *Algæ* possess chlorophyll and derive their energy therefore direct from sunlight. *Yeasts* are microscopic plants lacking chlorophyll and hence are forced to derive their energy by breaking up organic compounds previously synthesized by other means. *Fungi* are like the yeasts; their simple forms are known as molds. *Bacteria* are the smallest of these plant micro-organisms; in fact many are ultra-microscopic. As they possess no chlorophyll they too must obtain their energy by breaking down organic compounds built up by other living organisms. *Protozoa* are microscopic one-celled animals and move about at will in quest of food.

All of these microscopic forms of life may be further classified as *Saprophytes*,—a hardy pioneer race that derive their food by oxidizing inert organic matter—they include chiefly the yeasts, fungi and some bacteria; or *Parasites*,—deriving their food by attacking living cells—such are some bacteria and the protozoa.

THE FOUR HORSEMEN

Were it not for the microscopic organisms in the soil our plant life would be smothered out. These organisms must break up the residual organic wastes everywhere in order that the latter may be in proper condition for reabsorption by plant rootlets. Under average conditions good soil carries from one-half to one ton of these micro-organisms per acre, or anywhere from 100 to 250 billion micro-organisms per pound of soil. The energy developed by these organisms in each acre of well fertilized soil is calculated as about the equivalent of that exercised by twelve men, and the work accomplished by these same organisms as shown by plant growth above each acre of ground is sufficient to supply food requirements for two men.

The mineral salts in the soil together with certain of the decomposition products of plants, especially what are called the humic acids, determine the character of any soil and its distinct colloidal nature such that advantages for any particular class of plants may be at hand.

Where chemical conditions primarily hold sway in photosyntheses proceeding within the plant cells we now observe physical conditions are paramount within the soil if the chemical and biological reactions are ever later to materialize.

The condition of the soil thus becomes of far-

THE FARM CHEMURGIC

reaching importance in the stabilization of life on this planet. When conducive to plant growth we can attain any degree of luxuriance; when devoid of nutriment and microscopic life desert sands alone will be the reward.

Carbon dioxide and water have been seen to be the essentials to plant structure. Of them and their condensation products nearly the whole of all living forms are composed, certainly 90 per cent of all life is but carbon hydrogen and oxygen and when the element nitrogen is included this value is well over 95 per cent.

Now carbon dioxide exists in our atmosphere to the extent of three to four parts in 10,000 by volume. Small though this is the winds waft this gaseous compound hither and thither till they bring it in touch with every living leaf. The leaves, covered with rain or dew, absorb this gas especially during the night and together these products enter the chemical units of the plant laboratories at the rising of the sun.

Sunlight is the fourth factor,—and by far the most necessary to complete the team of four—which we may term the Four Horsemen—that gather the forces of this earth and direct them to man's ends.

It is here that we may relate our "four horsemen" to the basic "elements" of the Greek philosophers.

THE FOUR HORSEMEN

As with these early thinkers, "Earth," "Air," "Water," and "Fire," virtually encompass the whole of our living world. Though not the ultimate forms of matter they nevertheless constitute the four essential agencies that make for the origin and maintenance of life. "Earth" comprehends a nutritious soil abounding in microscopic life; "air" comprehends an oxygen, nitrogen, and carbon dioxide supply; "water" brings moisture to foliage and to soil; and "fire" denotes the sunlight of proper actinic rays.

If Aristotle's "quintessence" must likewise be given a counterpart in this modern version then the cosmic rays may well play this part.

Now the control of these four horsemen has been left pretty much to Fate. Certainly the sun and the air are beyond man's jurisdiction. The soil likewise has been regarded largely as an uncontrollable factor. But water, supplementing rain, is slowly coming under complete dominance by man. Up to the present we have been most remiss in this; but favorable signs now loom upon the horizon.

If we were to direct our millions of unemployed solely to construction of dams and waterways years upon years would pass ere the tasks could be completed. And none of the expenditures would be in vain as the ends will justify any means and constitute the most valuable asset any country can ever achieve.

THE FARM CHEMURGIC

The control of water makes possible the control of soil; recognizing of course that we are abundantly able to supply all necessary plant nutriment thereto. When water and soil come under man's control then and then only can we be said to be taking our part in the upbuilding of humanity; then too as we progress here we shall not fail to gain control over the air as regards carbon dioxide supply.

The four horsemen hold all living things in the palms of their hands. Their control over life is supreme. We cannot oppose them; such is synonymous with destruction and presages an Armageddon of catastrophe. We dare not supplicate them; such is to acknowledge defeat and go the way of peoples of old who perished in spite of all their sun gods and rain gods. The brave and manly thing is to acknowledge their power and enter into close coöperation with them.

We need not be the dumb driven animals we are today. All power is given into our hands if we will properly apply it. Try as the foolish will try the four horsemen cannot be thwarted. It is our duty therefore to bend all effort to bring these great agencies to bear on all mundane things such that man and his associates shall prosper and dwell together in peace and abundance; and the farm holds the key to this abundance.

CHAPTER VI

Chemical Life Cycles

WITHIN the soil is a vast storehouse of living and inanimate matter. The latter is made up chiefly of carbonates, sulphates, oxides and silicates of various metals together with silicon dioxide (quartz or sand) itself. About these siliceous particles cling oxides of iron as well as clay and other colloidal coatings. The great bulk of organic colloidal material in the soil is that which results from decomposition of plant and animal life; it makes up what is usually termed humus.

But the living organisms within the soil constitute a world of activity by themselves. They make their home in the gelatinous highly water-absorbing colloidal coatings that surround the coarser inorganic particles. Some of these micro-organisms require a large supply of oxygen or air with which to carry out their oxidation processes; these are called *"Aërobic."* Other organisms that can live deeper down in the soil need scarcely any oxygen to serve their purpose; these are called *"Anaërobic."*

In that bacteria contain no chlorophyll they are unable to invoke the aid of the sun for the building

THE FARM CHEMURGIC

up of carbohydrates from carbon dioxide and water; hence for their growth a definite supply of sugars, proteins and salts must be in constant supply. There is known one bacterium, Bacillus oligocarbophilus, that can utilize carbon monoxide (the half-way combustion product of carbon and oxygen, CO) and water for production of sugars, and another, Bacillus methanicus, that can make similar use of methane or marsh gas (the completely hydrogenated form of carbon, CH_4, or our first hydrocarbon).

A special class of bacteria can live by chemical decomposition of inorganic substances; these are called *Autotrophic* bacteria. They need no sunlight nor organic matter to aid them. In order to assimilate carbon dioxide and water for synthesis of food supply they derive the energy to this end by oxidation of hydrogen sulphide to sulphur. Another form oxidizes ferrous salts to ferric salts, and yet another oxidizes ammonia (NH_3) to nitrogen. By the labors of such bacteria we have been given those great beds of sulphur and iron ore. Particularly do we note here the ability of these bacteria to live on inorganic matter independently of any other living forms. They derive their energy by internal shifts within structure of inorganic material acted upon; thus they may have preceded all other forms of life on

CHEMICAL LIFE CYCLES

this planet in the barren state of its beginning and midst the sulphurous vapors that then enveloped it.

Micro-organisms grow through absorption of foods through their cell walls. Bacteria in particular require a high degree of moisture in the soil where they live. A moderate temperature (around 25 degrees C.) is considered preferable and more or less absence of light. Ultra-violet light in particular is highly destructive to all micro-organisms. Antiseptics likewise are highly destructive. Thus chlorine, a powerful death spreading agent against bacteria, has become a recognized purifier of city water supplies. Against various antiseptics there is further observed a certain selective destructivity such that the employment of definite varieties of micro-organisms can be predicated even in face of seemingly untenable conditions.

In the humus,—that residuum of all that was once plant or animal, but now in all stages of decomposition—we find a tendency toward acidity. The acids arising here are called humic acids. They are chiefly derivatives of polynuclear benzene hydrocarbons wherein the substituent group is the well-known carboxyl (–COOH) radicle typifying all organic chemical acids. The presence of lime is called for if this acidity is to be reduced.

Though many anaërobic bacteria slowly attack

THE FARM CHEMURGIC

cellulose and starch it is now known that these more or less insoluble carbohydrates are readily attacked in aërated soils; several micro-organisms have been found capable of fully oxidizing filter paper (pure cellulose) under aërobic conditions within three weeks. In certain sandy soil, especially in warm climates, the rapidity of oxidation carried on by micro-organisms under aërobic conditions completely eliminates all organic humus; thus desert conditions come into existence.

As carbohydrates and plant proteins are consumed by animals we note a considerable oxidation of much of the carbohydrates into water and carbon dioxide,—the latter exhaled through the lungs, whereas the plant proteins to a large extent are broken down in such manner as will permit of their further condensation into new and more complex types of protein,—now called animal protein.

The *Carbon Cycle* in life is now readily traceable. All carbonaceous waste when left to itself either above or below the surface of soil slowly decays; this is a slow combustion. Within the soil those micro-organisms called fungi attack cellulosic and cellular matter in general, and break down cell walls. Next the bacteria advance and reduce the entire mass to humus, and later other bacteria decompose this humus into simple compounds eventually cul-

CHEMICAL LIFE CYCLES

minating in carbon dioxide and water. The carbon dioxide thus set free accumulates in the air and to some extent in the soil.

The *Carbon Cycle* embraces the following stages:
(1) Carbon dioxide with water in Photosynthesis:
—Carbohydrates.
(2) Carbohydrates eaten by animals, or decomposed:—Carbon dioxide.

A large portion of plant life in past ages was laid down under impervious mineral strata and came under increasing pressure. Decomposition of these beds has given us our coal. In similar manner the decomposition of myriads of marine organisms under subsiding strata has given us petroleum. Micro-organisms are still functioning in the oceans to withdraw carbon dioxide and as they die there is built up a greater and greater deposit of chalk, limestone, and coral. Happily we have working against this carbon dioxide withdrawal a vast operation of weathering which is constantly decomposing limestone and carboniferous rocks.

The *Nitrogen Cycle* in life is much like the carbon cycle.
(1) Nitrates within the soil are absorbed through roots of plants and converted into nitrites and these into amino compounds and then into plant proteins.

(2) Plant proteins digested by animals are converted partly to animal proteins.

(3) Animal proteins are broken down in digestion by other animals and excreted partly as urea or similar type of compound, or are decomposed by decay into simple compounds.

(4) Ammonifying bacteria resolve all simple nitrogen compounds into ammonia.

(5) Ammonia reoxidized into nitrites and then into nitrates by nitrifying bacteria and the cycle repeats.

Some of the ammonia is converted into free nitrogen through chemical and biological agencies and thus becomes lost into the air. However, on the roots of leguminous plants (clover, peas and alfalfa) there exist nodules containing a nitrogen-fixing bacteria, capable of directly converting atmospheric nitrogen into nitrogen compounds. Even some of the molds, as those found on the roots of the alder, are likewise capable of fixing nitrogen. There occur several types of organisms within the soil itself (as Azotobacter chroöcoccum) that are able to convert free nitrogen direct into nitrogen compounds. Upon their death the soil is left enriched in nitrogen. Fallow land is enriched by just this action. The seeding of land to clover and final plowing under of this clover for conversion to humus enriches the land in

CHEMICAL LIFE CYCLES

fixed nitrogen to the extent of about 50 pounds per acre.

The *Sulphur Cycle* is likewise well established.

(1) When protein-like substances containing sulphur are left to decay the action of certain bacteria convert the sulphur completely into its reduced form or that of hydrogen sulphide (H_2S).

(2) Another class of bacteria now oxidize hydrogen sulphide back into sulphur and then into sulphuric acid (H_2SO_4). This acid acts in the soil to render soluble the more difficultly soluble forms of calcium phosphate, and is taken up again into combination with carbohydrate and protein to yield organic sulphur complexes.

An *Iron Cycle* is likewise known. Certain bacteria possess a sheath-like envelope containing ferric hydroxide; at death mounds of myriads of granules of iron ore give evidence of their earlier existence.

In the reactions set up by certain micro-organisms, both in the soil and out, we note the presence of substances occurring in minute proportions. About the middle of the past century Louis Pasteur, in Paris, observed that fermentation of sugar is a part of the life process of yeast. This means that the building up of yeast cells calls for energy which is secured through breaking down of carbohydrate molecules

THE FARM CHEMURGIC

into alcohol and carbon dioxide. Finally in 1897 E. Buchner in Germany dried some yeast and then took up the dried mass in water and filtered it through fine clay. The clear filtrate contained no yeast cells but nevertheless fermented sugar as did living yeast itself. The contents of normal yeast cells therefore constitute the active agent and act as catalyst for the fermentation of carbohydrates.

We now know a number of such organic catalysts (called here "soluble ferments") as are produced by bacteria and by living plants and animals. They have been given the name of *enzymes* (from the Greek word meaning *in leaven*). That enzyme occurring in ordinary yeast and capable of converting glucose into ethyl alcohol and carbon dioxide is called *Zymase*.

The enzymes as a class are readily kept in supply by their individual mother substance. They are little understood chemically. The reaction for alcoholic fermentation of glucose indicates two-thirds of the carbon content passes into alcohol and one-third of the carbon is lost as carbon dioxide:

$$C_6H_{12}O_6 \rightarrow 2\ CO_2 + 2\ C_2H_5OH$$
(Glucose) (Carbon dioxide) (Alcohol)

The reaction for the souring of wine (acetic fermentation) proceeds with the intake of oxygen and is as follows:

CHEMICAL LIFE CYCLES

$$C_2H_5OH + O_2 \rightarrow CH_3.COOH + H_2O$$
(Alcohol) (Oxygen) (Acetic acid) (Water)

Such process naturally will best proceed at the surface of liquid where air abounds.

Another well-known enzyme is that contained in sprouting barley (malt). This enzyme, *Amylase,* is capable of converting starch into glucose and maltose, two sugars that readily undergo alcoholic fermentation with yeast. Starch alone is not directly fermentable into alcohol under these conditions.

Ordinary cane (or beet) sugar (sucrose) is formed by the loss of one molecule of water between a molecule of glucose and a molecule of fructose (levulose). An enzyme known as *invertase* can readily hydrate this sucrose back into the two constituent sugars, glucose and fructose, and this mixture of resulting sugars is called *invert sugar*. It is said that invertase can hydrolyze one million times its weight of cane sugar without much loss in activity.

Throughout all life processes we have observed that those enzymes capable of resolving one class of compounds into another are likewise capable of turning the latter back into the former, that is, reversing the process. Primarily to this trait do we owe the ready distribution of sugars to the various parts of growing plants and at the same time their conversion

THE FARM CHEMURGIC

into starch and insoluble material for storage. When a demand for food arises at any one point these same enzymes must resolve starch at storehouse into sugar and transport it to desired location.

It is the cellulose that makes up the cellular structure of a growing plant; it is formed through a certain type of dehydration of the glucose molecule and possesses distinctly fibrous structure. As the plant matures its cellulose becomes associated with *lignin*, a special type of degradation product of sugars, and a sort of compact interlaced material results; this is called *wood*. Now lignin is a derivative of the benzene class of compounds and actually possesses antiseptic qualities, thus rendering wood more or less toxic to the action of micro-organisms. Were it not for this fortuitous arrangement our trees would succumb more rapidly to bacterial attack; or in effect would slowly dissolve in the rain.

Equilibrial conditions prevailing in life processes are of course subject to all manner of vicissitudes,—temperature, acidity or alkalinity of media, and even the mere presence of inorganic salts. It is well known that the work of a particular enzyme continues in its predestined direction,—constantly decomposing the material at hand (called substrate) till there is built up such a concentration of decomposition products

CHEMICAL LIFE CYCLES

that these latter in turn will inhibit the further action of the enzyme. Thus with alcoholic fermentation a concentration of about 15 per cent alcohol inhibits further action of yeast.

In general we may describe these enzymes as the agencies that enable living matter to grow and develop and carry out at lowest temperatures those prescribed chemical reactions necessary for continued existence.

Again we meet with other chemical substances whose chief service it is to regulate the functions of the living body. The vegetable world manufactures that class of compounds known here as *vitamins* and the animal world manufactures chiefly *hormones* to this end. These both must be in continuous supply and in proper proportions if higher forms of life are to be kept within normal size and functions.

When we contemplate the power of the four horsemen and their control over life on this planet it is clearly evident that microscopic organisms within the soil are destined to break down the organic complex that falls to earth and resolve it into such simple end-products as carbon dioxide, water, and ammonia. It is destined likewise that macroscopic organisms (notably man) above the soil shall break down the organic complex that emerges from earth and re-

THE FARM CHEMURGIC

solve it also into these same simple substances. Thus the cycles of life are made continuous.

To intelligent man is given the power voluntarily to interrupt the chemical degradation of organic matter such that intermediate stages may be utilized to his own betterment. These stages comprehend at present only the simplest hydrocarbons, alcohols, acids, and amino compounds. As civilization advances greater and greater will be the complexity of these intermediate compounds and more and more particularized to human needs the energy that is evolved in their final resolution into the simple end-products above named.

The energy that supports animal life comes directly from chemical transformations accompanying these degradation steps as just mentioned. Without proper functioning of microscopic organisms the entire vegetable world could not reproduce itself; in turn man himself could not emerge from chemical vapor.

In a sense the state and federal governments, in their greed to tax all tangible property to the utmost, are doing not otherwise than attacking the goose that lays the golden eggs. Microscopic life within the soil is made to suffer by neglect; microscopic life above the soil is given carte blanche to

CHEMICAL LIFE CYCLES

destroy all that man produces! Our sottish officialdom should certainly tax air, water, and sunlight, then their folly would be consummated. No longer does normal man question the utter stupidity that characterizes our would-be leaders; no longer does he doubt the bitter gloom and despair that is likely to overtake us if we do not purge our ways.

CHAPTER VII

The Wreck of the Farm Cycle

A STUDY of life cycles is necessary to an understanding of animate matter. As we proceed from lower to higher types we witness a waxing diversity in life cycles contributory to the perpetuation of a given species till in man we encounter a diversity and complexity that surpasses understanding. Furthermore in man a directive intelligence plays no unimportant rôle. The introduction here of the element of work defines what is known as industry in the broader sense; through its accomplishments we owe the upbuilding of man's physical, moral and mental status.

Mining, agriculture, and manufacturing taken together with transportation comprise the basic activities of mankind. Strictly speaking we can classify all under agriculture and industry. In each of these two great divisions a distinct cycle of operations functions to the maintenance of that division. We shall call the first the Agricultural or Farm Cycle, the second the Industrial Cycle.

The sequence of activities that makes up the farm

THE WRECK OF THE FARM CYCLE

cycle is built around the farmer and his labor. The delivery of power on the part of man and beast is registered in greater requirements of food on the part of the workers. This means a speeding up particularly in the carbon and nitrogen life cycles. As discussed previously, this indicates simply a speeding up in reduction-oxidization steps as applied to the simple sugars, such as glucose, supplied by the blood stream to all parts of the body. The chemical result of such action is lactic acid produced within the tissues and motive energy recorded without.

For the continued production of power to do work it is absolutely essential that the blood, in serving the muscles, be plentifully supplied with proper foods. In other words, the animal doing the work must be properly and timely fed and rested. The accumulation of lactic acid within muscle tissue gives rise to the tired feeling following labor. During rest periods much of this lactic acid is reconverted into glycogen by the muscles; the remaining portion is carried to the liver.

By application of this principle to the beasts of burden our ancestors, from Neolithic times, were able to develop power plants at will. The ox or horse was fed starch, cellulose, and proteins and allowed to rest; then placed before the plow or other implements for labor and made to perform his daily task,

THE FARM CHEMURGIC

whereupon he was re-fed, re-rested, and ready again for work. To sum up this physico-chemi-biological activity the farmer was able to develop power out of oats and corn and apply it at points desired.

In proper estimate of the work accomplished by power developed in the horse through eating of food we must have some tangible results, otherwise the cycle is not overly efficient; if left only to itself the horse would lead only to a continuation of horse. When, however, the horse is properly directed in work the accomplishments will more than warrant the cost of horse upkeep. Such will lead on the farm to what is known as "marketable surplus"; this is the direct measure of what we shall call a positively operating farm cycle.

Now a positively operating cycle is one that operates in the black, as ordinarily expressed, and leads to profit for the operators. In fact a Social Cycle may be set apart from the farm cycle, but closely meshed therewith, to picture more clearly the profit incentive. This completed circle in our social system comprehends skill through education followed by investment and proper management over such enterprise such that it will yield a profit. Furthermore, the expenditures from such earnings will be made to improve one's skill such as will lead to better investments. It is this latter that supplies the motivation of

THE WRECK OF THE FARM CYCLE

the farm. In other words, the social cycle activates the farm cycle.

We may depict the farm and its social cycle as shown in Figure 1.

Now the marketable surplus is that portion of the farm output that should meet with demand in the open markets. The unmarketable produce is left to be consumed on the farm both by human residents thereon as well as by beasts of burden; such material, therefore, is constantly on the way towards producing more power or undergoing chemical changes into other marketable material.

There is further a replenishment of the soil through a by-product in this cycle represented by the offal of animals. This highly desirable nitrogenous fertilizer is always in demand on the farm both as supplier of fixed nitrogen and decomposing humus.

The real output of the farm, therefore, is measured by the oversupply in organic chemicals grown on the land and which occur in excess of all requirements for such chemicals toward continuation of said farm in active service. In times of national plenty, as regards agricultural staples, the efficient farm units may well be maintained in almost dormant state and actually to improvement of the farm and the farmers, if there were no taxation curse placed upon them. But it is becoming increasingly difficult to hold

93

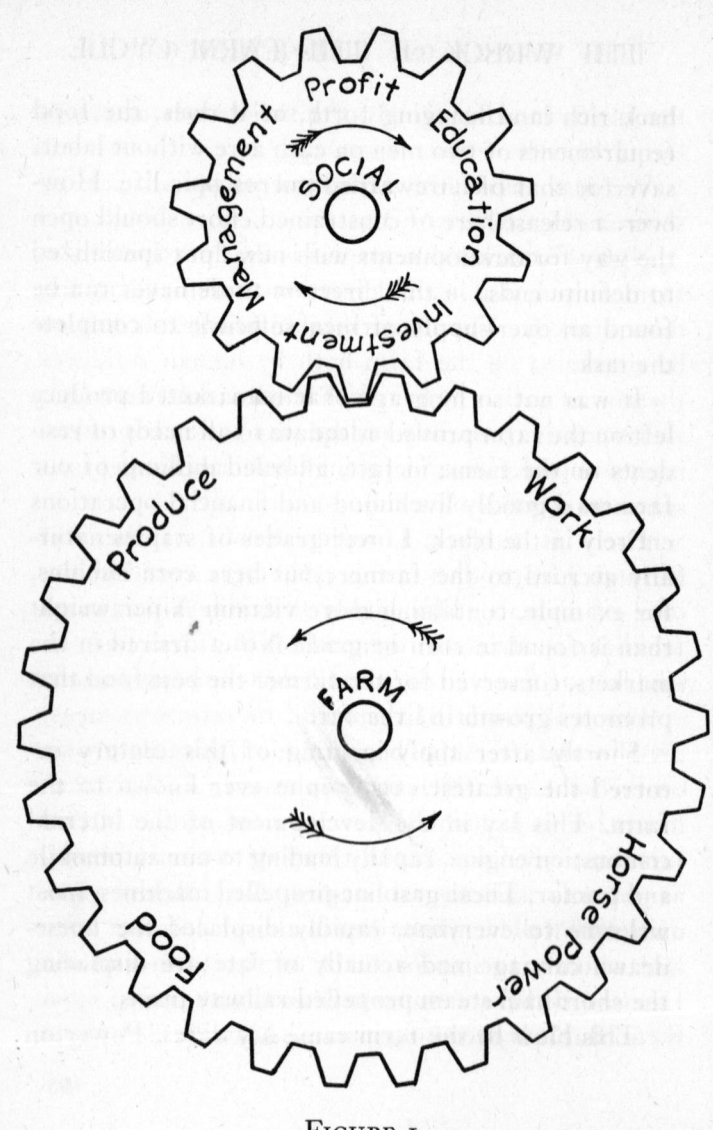

FIGURE 1

THE WRECK OF THE FARM CYCLE

back rich land bringing forth, as it does, the food requirements of two men on each acre without labor, save for that of unrewarded microscopic life. However, a release here of constrained effort should open the way for developments with new flora specialized to definite ends; in this direction there never can be found an over-supply of men sufficient to complete the task.

It was not so long ago that unmarketed produce left on the farm proved adequate to all needs of residents on the farm; in fact, afforded millions of our farmers a goodly livelihood and financial operations entirely in the black. Lower grades of staples naturally accrued to the farmer; but here corn nubbins, for example, containing more vitamin A per weight than is found in corn of grade No. 2 desired in the markets, conserved for the farmer the best food that promotes growth in livestock.

Shortly after the beginning of this century occurred the greatest catastrophe ever known to the farm. This lay in the development of the internal combustion engine, rapidly leading to our automobile and tractor. These gasoline-propelled machines, most welcome to everyone, rapidly displaced the horse-drawn carriage and actually of late are displacing the short-haul steam-propelled railway trains.

This blow to the farm came unawares. Power on

THE FARM CHEMURGIC

the farm heretofore took its rise in the secondary produce of the farm—that material falling below market requirements both in quality and quantity and hence of little or no pecuniary value. Such power thus arising out of low-priced foods carried a low price per horse-power unit. And the by-product fertilizer was worth more than the low-priced food intake per animal. Power on the farm, therefore, stood at lowest possible cost.

The introduction of the gasoline-power unit brought on the catastrophe. Slowly but surely the horse passed out of the picture. The secondary farm produce was forced into other animals such as the hog, but the markets became so glutted with pork that no profit could be made. Since 1920 the horse and mule population of the United States has dropped by 8,600,000 or by over 37 per cent; calculations based upon 3.5 acres as the average crop land required for feeding each horse, give slightly over 30,000,000 acres as hereby released from necessary cultivation.

If the automobile and tractor could be made to consume powdered cellulose and starch, as cornstalk and corn, there might appear some ray of hope. Farm produce, however, carries siliceous and other gritty material and is altogether unsuited for combustion in chambers of closely fitting and moving

THE WRECK OF THE FARM CYCLE

parts. And even here the fertilizer phase would be entirely lacking. The great difficulty attending any general use of farm produce in the rough is, of course, transportation. Such material is always bulky and subject to no end of decay and decomposition.

Thus came about the wreck of the farm cycle. For centuries upon centuries the power required on the farm was developed from waste products left on the farm and at little or no expense save in the care of draft animals. Our civilization took its rise with the dawn of agriculture witnessed in the taming of animals and cultivation of land by their aid. Yet here in one fell swoop within a single decade—1920-1930 —the wreck has been complete.

Second-class produce that supplied food for the horse now gave way to gasoline that supplied food for the machine. This constituted a sort of shunt or cut-off in the farm cycle. And as this deviation must function or run in the same plane as the original farm cycle, it may well be shown as a concentric cycle within the original cycle. Furthermore, the original cycle was now forced to show an extra profit to permit of the purchase of gasoline and machine, as neither of these in any way originate on the farm. But with a lessening demand for farm produce, naturally there could be no increase in profit and the

THE FARM CHEMURGIC

break was forced upon us; this indicates an operation in the red, or general failure.

Figure 2 will illustrate the change instituted.

Adding greatly to the distress occasioned on the farm in the wreck of the farm cycle we must not overlook the baneful influence that has accompanied this craze to acquire a gasoline-propelled machine. To this and similar wants we owe the increase in mortgages on the farms as well as on property in general. When taxes and interest on mortgages converge to point of oppression, we have the worst possible conditions that face our civilization. This is our predicament today.

Under such oppressed conditions the farms are operated to their fullest capacity no matter what the effect on the farm soil. This, as previously stated, offers the only way out. The mad money-lenders haven't sense enough to reduce their loans by at least 50 per cent—this is the average reduction in fertility of soil within the last five years—nor their interest rates by 50 per cent—bearing in mind that $3\frac{1}{4}$ per cent is all that money at interest has earned on the average through the centuries ever since the days of Rome; nor have the state and county authorities gumption enough to build up their farm properties by elimination of the tax curse.

In this connection we should all bear in mind that

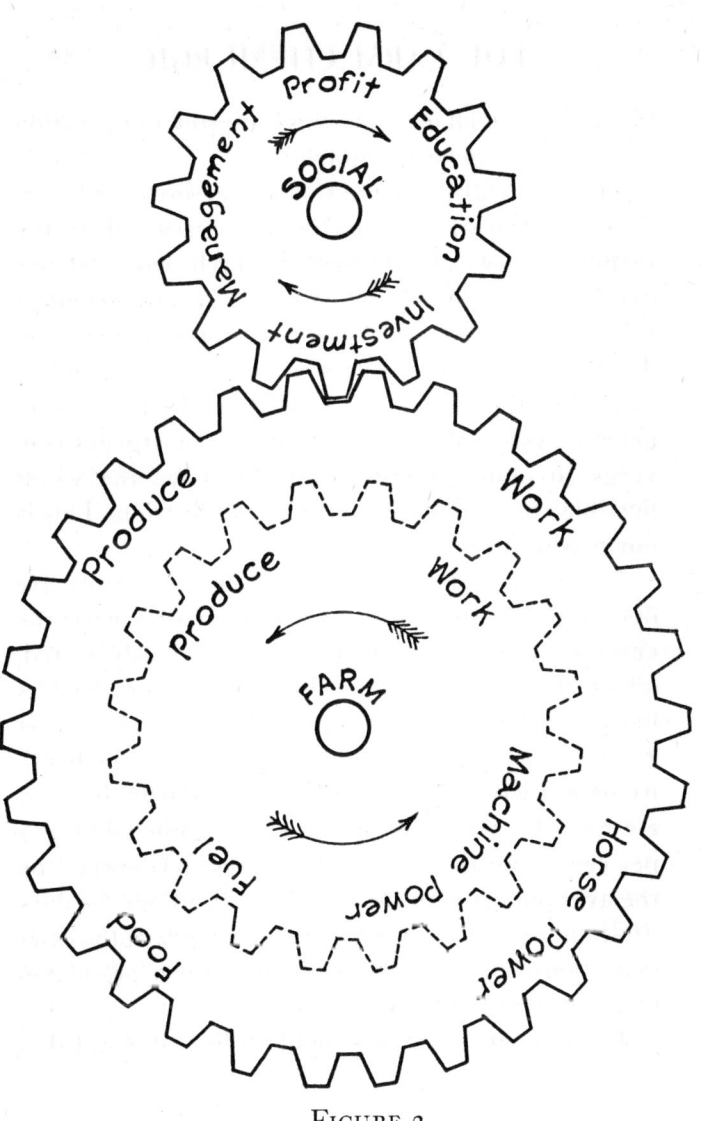

FIGURE 2

THE FARM CHEMURGIC

there is nothing more sacred attached to a note secured by mortgage on land than there is to one secured by preferred stock in a manufacturing corporation. Both share alike in the vicissitudes of a chemical world. Those who would think otherwise still believe in elves and fairies. A mortgage on a farm that is run down physically, chemically, and biologically carries little value whatsoever. If water could be impounded to cover such farm, a much greater value would accrue to it by way of fish pond.

Of the many factors that have contributed to mortgages and indebtedness among our citizens, amounting now to some $6,000,000,000 on the farms and $21,000,000,000 on home property in general, nothing possibly has had greater influence than asinine supersalesmanship. This is some sort of an art practiced by the semi-intelligent wherein a man is made to believe he wants what he never wanted before and usually when he gets it he never wants it again. The supersalesman is a bane to modern society. His piffle is what you are more than likely to hear over the radio in this country every day unless you are clever enough to cut it off. Only a fool will buy his wares. Through him, no doubt, much of recent indebtedness on the farm has been incurred. Modern Germany has taken a forward step for elimination of all such drawbacks to the farmer:—

THE WRECK OF THE FARM CYCLE

no longer can farm lands be mortgaged. So should it obtain here. If you want to sell to a farmer, his personal note should be amply sufficient. In honor he certainly outranks both salesman and shopkeeper.

The wreck of the farm cycle is rendered thus all the more harrowing by the plight of the farmer bent down by excessive debt and by lowered prices on farm products, occasioned primarily by the best of efforts on the part of the farmer to pay off his debts by the sweat of his brow. This is the picture before us now. It has become more poignantly impressed upon us since the early days of this century. It has existed in a sense since the passing of the last frontier.

Our national and state governments have certainly devoted much time to the study of this question; and always do we find vast sums of money poured out to relieve the downtrodden farmer and humble home owner.

Farm leaders have been called into conferences and farm organizations asked for advice. Economists have been given authority to outline workable procedures, and yet in spite of all these things nothing has been of real help to the farmer. His plight grows steadily worse.

CHAPTER VIII

The Wreck of the National Cycle

INDUSTRIAL life, in stricter sense, is concerned primarily with those activities that lie beyond the farm. It takes its rise both in the products of the mines and the farm and develops its output to meet all demands. There is here discernible a periodicity of functions that may well be characterized as the Industrial Cycle.

The sequence of activities that makes up the industrial cycle is built around the industrialist and his labor. The industrial cycle, just as the farm cycle, is activated by a social or profit cycle. Furthermore coördinated with the industrial cycle there are a number of smaller cycles as integral parts thereof, and which must not be confused therewith. Thus, for example, we may cite the cycle of manufacture: This cycle embraces raw products, basic manufacture, finished article and junk and back again to raw products. The waste in all manufacturing steps, as well as much of the junk, is worked up again through basic manufacture. The greater portion of waste re-entering this cycle has always consisted chiefly of metals

THE WRECK OF THE NATIONAL CYCLE

and the products of mines. Indeed this is exactly what might be expected in an industrial age starting as it did with mass production of steel.

The industrial cycle is closely akin to the agricultural or farm cycle. Merchandise manufactured and sold enables the industrialist to purchase food which when consumed by the individual develops power, both physical and mental, and this power accomplishes work; through this work more merchandise is manufactured and the cycle is complete. This cycle coördinated with its social cycle may be depicted as in Figure 3.

Improvements in quality of manufactured goods are brought about by increased expenditures for labor, and improvements in price of such goods are brought about by greater efficiency of this labor. Now in an advancing civilization the individual has unlimited powers for learning and skill, hence the industrial cycle registers its efficiency in modernization of mechanical operations to fit the more skilled operators, thus reducing more and more the requirements for unskilled labor units. This, of course, is just another way of saying that the modernization of machinery throws men out of work.

Graphically we may interpret the effect of machinery installation within the industrial cycle as a sort of shunt or cut-off, whereby merchandise is sold

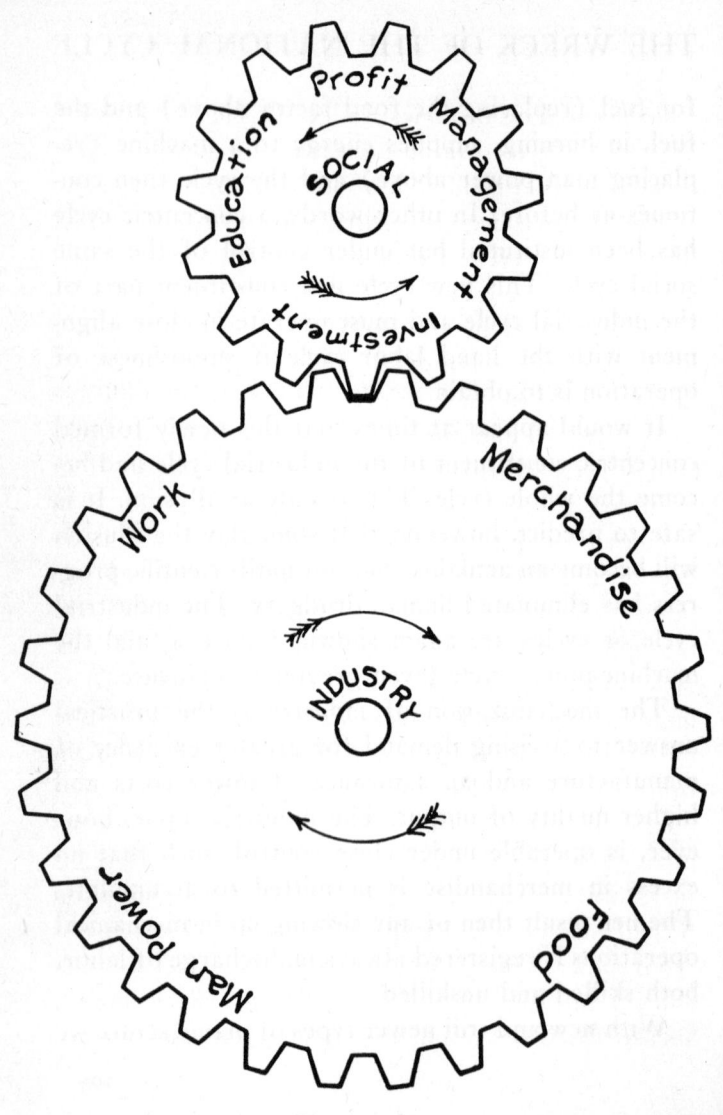

FIGURE 3

THE WRECK OF THE NATIONAL CYCLE

for fuel (replacing the food factor above) and the fuel, in burning, supplies energy to a machine (replacing man power above) and the cycle then continues as before. In other words, a concentric cycle has been instituted but under control of the same social cycle. This new cycle is a constituent part of the industrial cycle and must operate in close alignment with the hand labor cycle if smoothness of operation is to obtain.

It would appear at times that this newly formed concentric constituent of the industrial cycle had become the whole cycle. This is only an illusion. It is safe to predict, however, that some day the illusion will become an actuality, but not until scientific progress has eliminated human drudgery. The industrial cycle or cycles are again shown, Figure 4, and the machine-power cycle given greater prominence.

The mechanization of industry is the practical answer to a rising demand for greater efficiency of manufacture and an assurance of lower costs and higher quality of output. The industrial cycle, however, is operable under close control, such that no excess in merchandise is permitted to accumulate. The net result then of any slowing up in mechanical operations is registered always in discharge of labor, both skilled and unskilled.

With new and still newer types of manufacture we

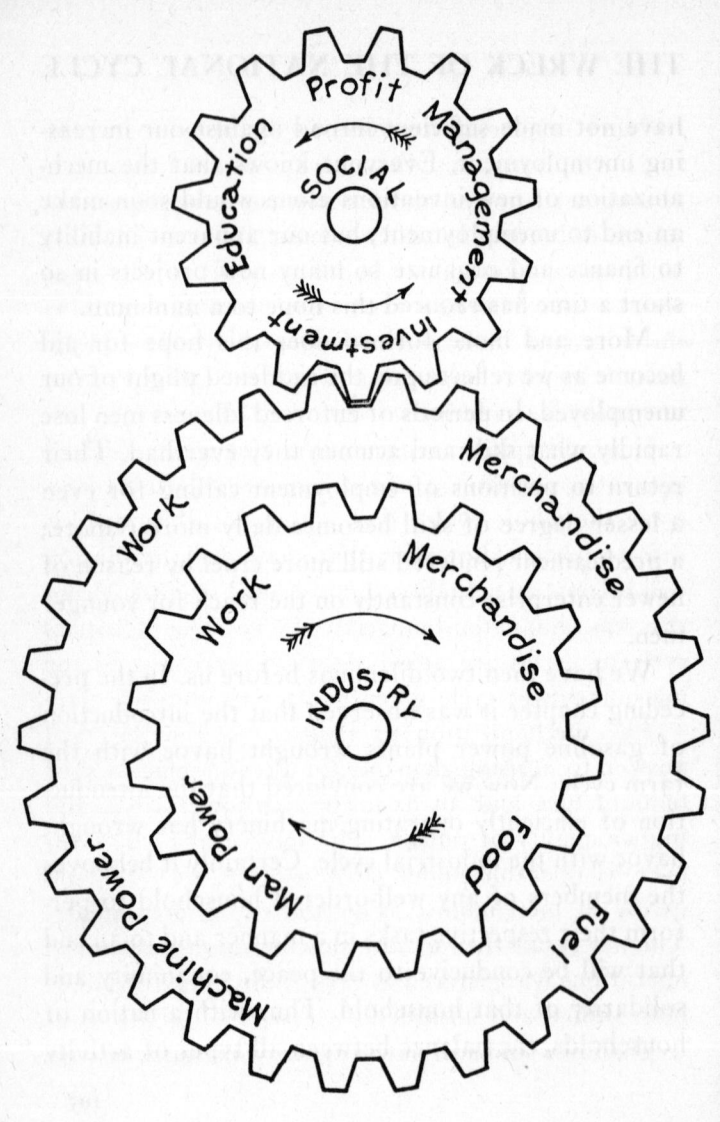

FIGURE 4

THE WRECK OF THE NATIONAL CYCLE

have not made sufficient inroad against our increasing unemployment. Everyone knows that the mechanization of new inventions alone would soon make an end to unemployment; but our apparent inability to finance and organize so many new projects in so short a time has reduced this hope to a minimum.

More and more forlorn does this hope for aid become as we reflect upon the saddened plight of our unemployed. In periods of enforced idleness men lose rapidly what skill and acumen they ever had. Their return to positions of employment calling for even a lesser degree of skill becomes daily more remote; a predicament rendered still more cruel by reason of newer enterprise constantly on the reach for younger men.

We have then two dilemmas before us. In the preceding chapter it was observed that the introduction of gasoline power plants wrought havoc with the farm cycle. Now we are convinced that the introduction of efficiently operating machinery has wrought havoc with the industrial cycle. Certainly it behooves the members of any well-ordered household to perform their respective tasks in a manner and to an end that will be conducive to the peace, equanimity and solidarity of that household. Thus with a nation of households, the balance between all types of activity

THE FARM CHEMURGIC

must be so maintained that peace, security and contentment will abound everywhere.

We are confronted, therefore, with the wreck of what may be called our "National Cycle." This cycle comprehends a balance in operation between production and consumption on the part of a nation. Within this cycle are many component cycles, but chief of all and engaging practically the entire gamut of activities of all inhabitants stand the farm and industrial cycles.

Today there is neither rhyme nor reason in attempts at coöperation between farm and factory. Each runs riot to its best ability with no concern whatsoever in the well-being of its friends or competitors. Citizens connected with these two all-embracive components of our national cycle,—the farm and industrial cycles—may actually be described as almost entirely estranged excepting when opportunity arises for gouging one another or giving vent to calumny of various sort. To say that these two component cycles are out of gear is far short of the truth; they are out of control and distorted beyond description:—the national cycle is on the rocks.

"Agricultural surplus and industrial unemployment running wild" may well be the heading for some future delineation of present-day scenes. But why has this state come upon us? What causes have

THE WRECK OF THE NATIONAL CYCLE

led up to it and under what circumstances can we right ourselves once more?

The real cause of the disparity between farm and industrial cycles lay in the progress of science itself and in our failing to incorporate its teachings into our workaday world. Metallurgy was making rapid strides even at the time of Watt's steam engine. Upon the introduction of the Bessemer furnace mass production came to the fore; but only after another decade or two did we have accuracy in metal castings sufficient to pave the way for the introduction into machinery of what is described as "replaceable parts."

Along with metallurgy, and virtually a prerequisite thereto, the opening up of vast coal mines and introduction of coking processes introduced the gas and lighting industries. Then came the petroleum industry, likewise originating in a type of mining. Both the coal and petroleum industries are nothing more than chemical industries, but during the greater part of the past century no one had any chemical knowledge of either coal or petroleum.

The development of fuels was almost wholly empirical. The invention of the internal combustion engine, during the last few years of the past century, created intensive interest in the processing of petroleum for more volatile hydrocarbons. The first few

THE FARM CHEMURGIC

years of this century brought us to extensive "cracking" of petroleum for gasoline.

Furthermore, the rapid progress in automobile manufacture called more and more upon metallurgist and engineer. Through their ingenuity we perfected the motor for higher and higher compression of explosive charge, improved all alloys entering the automobile, and tremendously extended the serviceability of rubber tires: In everything was progress but it concerned itself almost solely with inorganic chemistry.

Now the state of knowledge concerning organic chemistry was deplorable almost down to the close of the nineteenth century; especially in this country. Not till 1887 did Emil Fischer, in Berlin, succeed in unravelling the secrets by which nature synthesizes the most elementary of the sugars. All knowledge of plant growth prior to this date was nil.

Beginning with this century we record the greatest of all strides in organic chemistry. A knowledge of sugars, fats and oils was followed by knowledge of synthetic resins or plastics and silk-like fibre from cellulose. Slowly but surely the products of nature, that is, the farm, are yielding to man's ingenuity. But technical applications of these advances in organic chemistry did not get under way till the second decade of this century. In fact, it required a World War

THE WRECK OF THE NATIONAL CYCLE

before any general spread in organic chemical manufacture could be recorded.

Looking backward upon these two great cycles of our national life it becomes increasingly evident that the industrial cycle received a tremendous impetus at the beginning of this century whereas the farm cycle was following its accustomed course, and gradually losing in personnel. Then came the World War and both were speeded up beyond measure. Industries now called for aid and many left the farms for the factories.

Following the war totally abnormal conditions prevailed everywhere. Especially in this country have we experienced every sort of abnormality as relates to the proper coördination between farm and industrial activities. Raw products for industry were left to come from whatever sources were available but at lowest costs; which of course meant the mines, as here alone reasonably low costs of output prevailed.

The products of the farm, though inclusive of materials used in raiment and shelter, are particularly looked upon as food supply. During the war these food prices soared beyond all reason and during phantom prosperity days they again touched the ceiling. Certainly no reputable manufacturing organization could long exist if its source of supply were subject to such gyrations in quantity and price. Hence

THE FARM CHEMURGIC

more and more have we found our industries sticking closely to steady and reliable sources that lie outside the farmers' field.

The price uncertainty attaching itself to almost all farm produce has contributed more than all else of late to the banishment of the farm as a source of basic supplies for industry. There was never any reason for such turn of events. Good farm lands (and we have seen how all lands can be made into good farm lands) bring forth abundantly even by themselves and occasion no high costs in anything they produce under normal and scientific conditions. The prerequisite here of a liberal investment in fertilizers should not act as a deterrent when rich harvests and lower prices for total output can be assured.

But the craze that we can get something for nothing is too much for the mind of mediocre man to overcome. Why then should he invest in long time enterprise when petroleum, coal, minerals of all sorts, seemingly within easy reach, lay open to exploitation.

Now it is a well-known fact that the total financial outlay attending the mining of petroleum over the country as a whole, and inclusive of unsuccessful as well as successful ventures, is never equalled by total revenue accruing from sale of crude petroleum so mined; and likewise in the other mineral industries,

THE WRECK OF THE NATIONAL CYCLE

—the total selling price of raw products does not make up for total outlay in mining when all ventures are included. Yet in farm produce we actually can show a profit over cost of operation. Of course this profit is due largely to the four great agencies that control all:—the soil with its microscopic life, the air with its carbon dioxide, and the rain and the sun, —and no charge accompanies their labors. Ages ago these same agencies manufactured and collected our mineral wealth, but they laid it not at our doors.

In spite of all drawbacks man's knowledge of organic chemistry has been progressing with leaps and bounds. All agriculture is now in good understanding and bids fair to open unlimited possibilities for industrial utilization. By the opening of the third decade of this century the technicalization of organic chemical processes had become established in many isolated spots over the earth. Greater technicalization awaits only our own initiative.

No longer can we tolerate the wide fluctuations of the past as regards farm produce. Furthermore, all excessive transportation charges on agricultural waste must be eliminated by establishment of chemical processing plants in fair proximity to natural sources of supply. These agricultural centers—which we may call *Agricenters*—will undertake only the first steps in degradation of complex organic mix-

THE FARM CHEMURGIC

tures, such as cereals and the like, and send into transport lesser tonnage of partially purified material of greater stability.

When we come back to the farm and adjust farm produce for industrial use then and then alone shall we be able to establish mutually progressive activities in both farm and industry; this portrays a positively operating national cycle. If we look upon the farm and industrial cycles as geared wheels it will be necessary for these wheels to be in mesh if a close relationship is to be depicted; when so engaged these two great cycles will make for smooth performance of our national mechanism.

CHAPTER IX

The Ship of State Adrift

WE cannot have a smoothly functioning national cycle till the farm and industrial cycles are in perfect gear; a house divided against itself cannot stand. It is necessary, therefore, that every effort be directed toward bringing these two great activities of man into perfect coördination.

Many are the proposals put forth by economists and politicians looking to a betterment of this or that phase of the problem. Good results have followed many of the plans placed in operation. It is frightful, however, to contemplate the vast expenditures of money directed in countless channels opened up by such efforts. Thus far no accomplishment has revealed itself other than as a small step toward the final solution.

There is still extant a class of citizen who cherishes the hope that lowering of tariffs may in some way bring an increase in foreign trade, and to them foreign trade is a panacea for all national ills. They seem to overlook the fact that the foreign trade of all countries since the phantom prosperity days has dropped in the same degree as ours or to about one-third of former values. Particularly is this noteworthy when we recall that more than two-thirds of all our imports are on the free list; and the decline in trade affecting articles on the free list is slightly greater than with articles on the dutiable list.

What tariffs exist today both here and abroad are serving for protection of home industry and agriculture. The old-time cry of free trade is as dead as the dodo bird and has no greater chance than this bird of being resurrected. In pre-chemical days such folderol made interesting topic for debate in college and village circles; today it is indicative of non-chemical vision on the part of its advocates.

Each and every nation of self-respecting citizens is bringing itself as rapidly as possible to a state of self-containment. Have we any right to pronounce them dull just because they wish to restrict imports to a point below which their markets can absorb these imports without detriment to the activities of their own industries? The chemical revolution revealed to them just as it did to us the unlimitable adaptation of their own resources to practically all of their own needs.

Early this spring, in Italy, there was announced an increase in import duties and sales tax applicable to mineral oils and their products. At the same time

THE SHIP OF STATE ADRIFT

emphasis was laid upon total absence of excise and other taxes on vegetable oils for general industrial use. Need we look for better assurance of a scientific leadership that is directing Italy into agricultural prosperity?

This country has chosen to continue as an industrial nation. We entered this state at the close of the World War as we passed from a debtor nation of about $8,000,000,000 in 1916, to a creditor nation in 1920, when foreign nations owed us about $15,000,000,000.

Naturally we should not hamper international trade; but why magnify its significance beyond all dimensions. Such smacks of the logic of internationalists, according to whom it should be forever impossible for happiness and prosperity to obtain on earth till we have taken up trade with the inhabitants of Mars or some other planet. They can have nothing chemically over there that we haven't here, and the same applies to the great nations on our own planet.

It is right and proper that we take from one nation only about as much as that nation either directly or indirectly takes from us. To take more hinders our own development and to sell more to them is likely to interfere with their development. The golden rule is here deservedly applicable; especially now that we realize foreign loans henceforth will need to be se-

THE FARM CHEMURGIC

cured by liens on land and properties of nations concerned.

Our industrial status dictates our future to be that of an importer of agricultural products and exporter of manufactured goods. The reasons for this conclusion lie before us in the following chapters. When we get beyond our present mere pittance of exportable surplus in manufactured goods, amounting to about 6 per cent of our total manufacture, we may consider ourselves as about to be established in the export field. At all times export of manufactured goods must keep pace with import of manufactured goods or raw products; and our industrial trend points ever to raw products.

Thus are we forced to look adversely upon all those recent suggestions that invoke the selling of our agricultural surplus in foreign markets at any price. This could only bring stigma upon us and certainly not help our domestic situation in the end. If any peoples are in dire want let us give them of our plentiful supply. But why try to beat a foreign nation in a trade? We are mere infants at the game.

Foreign trade holds no sweet insouciance to our belabored citizens. The hope and salvation of our farmers lies not in this direction. In industry a reasonable export does await those articles of latest invention and commanding highest technique in

THE SHIP OF STATE ADRIFT

manufacture,—but only for the nonce; foreign producers will soon have acquired our art sufficient to supply the same objects at lower prices. By keeping ahead in invention, therefore, we shall have reasonable assurance of a proportionately greater increase in exportable merchandise.

Touching our agricultural situation we have been presented of late with a scheme that aims to reduce the need for import or export. It may be called the "Famine-Dole" plan. This plan proposes a cut in acreage under cultivation in order that a decrease in output shall bring about higher prices for products.

According to the 1930 census figures for this country there are some 6,000,000 farms embracing about 980,000,000 acres of land; under cultivation we have only 360,000,000 acres; out of this about 100,000,000 acres has lost its top soil. All told we have somewhat over 30,000,000 people living on the farm and of this number a little over 10,000,000 classed as gainfully employed. In the cities and villages there are about 90,000,000 citizens, of which number some 28,000,000 are gainfully employed and about 10,000,000 unemployed. Inclusive of villages of 2,500 and under, the rural population of this country comes to about 44 per cent of the whole; whereas the remaining, or 56 per cent, represents the urban population.

THE FARM CHEMURGIC

Up to the beginning of this century we were primarily an agricultural people. Our chief products were cotton, wheat, corn, and fruits and meats; along with these we manufactured sewing machines, reapers, plows and such things as farming people required. Then came our chemical awakening during the World War and we entered industrial status.

In reflections upon this pristine state there has ever been the feeling that the farm is the great provider of foods and raiment. A sort of cherished independence arises in the hearts of even the lowly that on the farm all wants can be supplied by the labor of man. This is the spirit that has contributed so commendably to American Independence. But upon scientific examination we find this is a mere trifle of what the farm is yet to be.

Chemi-biological study reveals how we may grow all manner of farm produce at lower costs and greater yields per acre. We have found recently that one may grow several crops of potatoes per year. But even without regard for such special measures we can so cultivate our farms as to bring forth a huge abundance of all things to all needs. Be this as it may, there is no necessity in cultivating anywhere near as much acreage as now cultivated in order to supply our foods.

Today we can garner from 100,000,000 acres of

THE SHIP OF STATE ADRIFT

our lands, under proper cultivation, all the produce required in supplying the citizens of the United States with their requisites in food and raiment and affording an abundant carry-over to the next season. In fact, about one farmer out of five can ably deliver to us all of our requirements in the way of food and raiment supply. As agriculture advances, in the light of chemi-biological study, we may confidently look forward five or six years when the total requirements of our citizens for foods and raiment will readily be supplied through intensive cultivation of a mere 50,000,000 acres of properly fertilized land.

What, then, is the future of the four out of five farmers who even now need work no more? What, likewise, is to be done with the two or three hundred million acres of land we need no longer cultivate? In the answers to these questions lies the real solution to the farm problem.

When we contemplate the famine-dole plan mentioned above we wonder what hallucinations must have come before the minds of its perpetrators. The proposal takes no consideration of taxes that are not removed nor of mortgages and rates of interest that are not lowered. Its operation would reduce our farmers to the lowest of the peasant class; many permitted only to grovel for existence and others left dependent upon alms. The proposal is debasing be-

THE FARM CHEMURGIC

yond measure and is destined, thank Heaven, to a disastrous end.

Oddly enough, the originators of the famine-dole plan never looked into the matter of direct conversion of excess farm produce into durable stores for future needs. Biblical history should be sufficiently remindful on this point. Possibly these novices felt we were above future famine and pestilence. And yet today we are facing the severest drought in years; furthermore, every indication points to more intensive drought in the season to come. Verily this plan of the infants-in-arms will make for famine ever dominant.

In the matter of increased prices for farm produce we come to the rock on which all farm measures heretofore have been wrecked. The farmer cares not for prices if he can only be assured a profit on what he can produce at will. This does not mean a rise in selling price. It may just as well signify a lowering in cost. And when the latter obtains, greater and greater will become the demand for such produce in a broadening market. The farmers want unlimited markets!

Throughout modern history there is no single case on record of where the manufacturer of an article has not been able to lower his costs of manufacture with the march of progress. The costs of raw products in a scientific world are always dropping and

THE SHIP OF STATE ADRIFT

where, perchance, there arises some scarcity in a needed raw material the manufacturer is quick to find a substitute which often proves to be even better than the original. History is replete with the story of the greedy who, all too willing to run up prices on their wares, suffered their own undoing when the demand for these wares was eliminated through introduction of something better as brought into existence through research and investigation. Witness the gouging of the American public on amber, coral, fossil gums, natural silk, camphor, iodine and countless such. Today we control our own sources or substitutes for all of these. Certainly those who advocate a rise for farm produce can have no comprehension of what scientific adaptations signify.

The great curse attaching itself to the famine-dole plan is contained in the discouragement it offers to all citizens on the land. It offers no incentive to better your crops or increase your yields. It encourages no competition which is the keynote to progress. It is not even a stop-gap to curb the tide of runaway supplies. Supplies are going to get cheaper and cheaper and cheaper no matter what governments may do. The people have a right to reap the benefits resulting from research and these benefits always lead to lowering in prices on all commodities.

When we come to industry there is just as much

THE FARM CHEMURGIC

difficulty attending this problem; but here it is primarily concerned with the unemployment situation. Merchandise, corresponding to staples from the farm, is here more or less under controlled production in keeping with the law of supply and demand. On the farm this situation can never be closely adjusted owing to the impotence of the present-day man. In the future it will be adjusted with ease, but that presages the advent of masculine masterly minded man (and we do not know such today).

The feeding of the unemployed by use of surplus from the farm is, of course, only a stop-gap. It will get nowhere save possibly to deaden all initiative on the part of those being fed; yet, thankfully, it will keep our destitute from starving. It dare not be continued for long. Correctly interpreted, the present procedure is nothing more than an attempt to bring the farm and industrial cycles in some sort of relationship, such as may be accomplished through feeding the surplus of the farm cycle to the unemployed of industrial cycle and helping generally to provide shelter and education for these unfortunates.

The dictum that this plan can never really help lies in the fact that, as previously stated, any sort of progress entails, from year to year, a decrease among agriculturists and industrialists requisite to accomplishment of stated tasks. Unemployment thus is

THE SHIP OF STATE ADRIFT

ever on the increase. It cannot be otherwise in an advancing civilization! Pauperism becomes therefore our goal and pending its attainment we are nourished by dole. Better far that we strike out at the root of the trouble and bend all efforts to establish complete coördination between farm and industrial cycles.

The only plan that can have any basis for consideration by thinking men must necessitate a meshing of agricultural or farm cycle with the industrial cycle. From another angle we may interpret the communication of motion between these two cycles as effected by endless belting over two wheels. All proposals so far have simply taken from one and handed to the other; whereas the correct idea is that work should be instituted in order for those of one cycle in this life to partake of the products of the second cycle, and the products of the first cycle must be used in turn by those of the second cycle. In the end all plans that cannot stand the closest of chemical and biological scrutiny, as is commensurate with our chemical and biological world, are of course doomed to failure. Broadly speaking, all by-products must come into definite use between these cycles.

The public works expenditures today require much labor and contribute to the upbuilding of the state. The idea is laudable but our distorted cycles are not hereby set into gear. So likewise with much of the

THE FARM CHEMURGIC

other work recently outlined. It is good but cannot solve the trouble. The training of young men in forest life is of especial merit and may actually be turned to direct scientific advantage.

We have spent so many millions and billions of dollars that one may rightly expect some sort of master stroke by this time out of the thousands that have been attempted. The problem, however, remains just as vexing as before. In fact we have not influenced the trend; we are drifting further to sea.

Can it be that our political leaders lack confidence in the Ship of State? Or is it just a spell of hypnotism cast over them by economists? Though economists talk the language of politicians and diplomats they are so unschooled in physics, chemistry, and biology as to be unable to discuss here the controlling factors affecting this national problem. In fact the entire structure of our Ship of State is physical, chemical and biological and no amount of study that eliminates the principles of these three sciences can ever be of directive influence in positive advance.

It is high time that we get down to plain facts and gather together trusted men without greed to serve as officers under the leadership of our President as Commander-in-Chief. This is naught else but a chemical world and we are adrift on a chemical sea. Our Ship of State makes little headway in devious

THE SHIP OF STATE ADRIFT

ways. The two big propellers, driven by mighty shafts proceeding each directly from one of the powerful activities of our national cycle, are out of control. Lately one propeller has been running at high speed and the other most of the time out of the water. To say that we progress in circles is self-evident; any other course would be well-nigh impossible.

Those in the engine room of our good ship display no knowledge of its intricate mechanical installations. To them machinery is just a moving design in wheels. They pour out lubricating oil on all movable parts (money thrown to ease the grit of criticism) and trust to Fate that the oil supply will not become exhausted. But yet no headway! We still move in circles!

Now the two components of our national cycle will not become properly engaged till we engage them. We have all the resources we shall ever need and there is abundant craftsmanship aboard. Why not, then, bring the various units of our mechanism into proper coördination. Thus and thus alone can we hope for harmonious performance and a steady forward progress of this great Ship of State.

CHAPTER X

Chemi-Biological Reckoning

THE proper functioning of the national cycle is dependent upon proper coördination of all activities that constitute this cycle. The two major activities are those of agriculture and industry, hence the farm and industrial cycles must be brought into perfect synchronization and harmony. Furthermore as our population is about equally divided between these two major activities we must prorate to equal degree their power to operate.

In order to direct the farm and industrial cycles such that their joint effect shall be transmitted positively to the progress of a nation these two cycles must be made mutually embracive both as to materials involved and individuals employed. This would signify a complete interlocking of farm and factory to the end that the products of the farm constitute in large measure the raw products of industry and the products of industry constitute in same degree the desiderata of the farm.

The interpretation here is based on what commerce between nations must become ere we have

CHEMI-BIOLOGICAL RECKONING

anything like rational trade. The great drawback to present-day international trade is the absence of a scientific and stabilized international monetary system; a drawback wholly lacking in commerce between component activities in any one nation. Consequently we should be in position to make better headway toward a rationalization of our own activities.

When operating in close relation, and each under its own activating or directive control, one may depict the farm and industrial cycles as two meshed wheels geared severally to their respective social cycles. Figure 5 is merely the composite of the broadened farm and industrial cycles earlier set forth.

The surplus from farm and industry must be largely consumed within farm and industry. Correctly speaking there should be no marketable surplus beyond that called for as storage against possible adversity and as equivalent in trade for raw products brought in from abroad.

Arguments that decry this state of affairs in the name of international trade are arguments to no avail in a scientific world. Everyone knows of commercial rivalries in the past and of the rise and fall of nations as a consequence thereof. Such "commercialism run riot" will little be tolerated in the future. Today all of the greater nations are intent upon chemically readjusting themselves to greater poten-

FIGURE 5

CHEMI-BIOLOGICAL RECKONING

tialities and especially as pertains to self containment. Let us reiterate: "This is the lesson of the great chemical revolution."

Of course there will be some international trade and happily so but, as heretofore expressed, it must be confined rather closely to necessary raw products save where a nation selling such raw products can take an equal value in finished goods.

Our industrialism precludes any extensive development of agriculture save to our own ends. This is exactly what coördination within the national cycle demands; and this therefore becomes the basis for any plan that will strengthen our agricultural and industrial relationship.

Reduced to simple terms this denotes that the raw products to be supplied industry must come more and more from the farm; that is, they must be increasingly organic. It further denotes that the raw products formerly in supply to industry must come less and less from the mines; that is, they must be less inorganic.

Again in common parlance this is nothing more than saying that houses and automobiles and trains and countless objects of workmanship must be constructed of wood or better of cellulose, lignin and their derivatives, but now in newly discovered noncombustible and durable form such that excels for

THE FARM CHEMURGIC

many purposes the old-fashioned metals so given to rust and corrosion. After all, this was the custom in years gone by and in years where contentment among civilians was more prevalent than today.

This doctrine does not teach that we are to do away with metals, cement, and the like. It merely emphasizes the necessity of a higher consumption of the organic compounds in relation to the inorganic compounds in all walks of life. We do not criticize those who have worked and planned to the end that as much from the mines be utilized as befits a rising civilization. Rather do we pity them for their lack of vision; yet here again there was little known a score of years ago that could give any basis for vision.

In the days just preceding the mechanical revolution those engaged in manufacture and trade did not outnumber those engaged in agriculture. Then too the total tonnage of products reaching the markets from the mines was not half the tonnage of products from the farm. Of course the introduction of coal and installation of blast furnaces brought about the change,—a period coincident with the rise of our industrial era.

Since the mechanical revolution the utilization of products from the mines has been proceeding with prodigious speed. Notably in recent years the introduction of petroleum has contributed greatly to this

CHEMI-BIOLOGICAL RECKONING

advance. Today we are astonished to find that the total tonnage of products in this country springing from mineral resources amounts to over one billion tons annually; whereas the total tonnage of products from our farms (inclusive of forests) does not exceed one-half billion tons. And in this latter tonnage no deduction is made for water content which runs so high in such products as fruits, vegetables and milk.

Strikingly apparent to all is this complete overturn in basic commodities as affecting industry and agriculture. Little more than a century has passed from the time when the ratio of mineral output to land output was as 1 to 2; today it is 2 to 1 respectively.

In order now to determine what this "mineral output" to "land output" ratio should be for any country it is only necessary to study the available acreage of that country. In an earlier chapter the effect of light on living plants has been discussed. For the temperate zone in forest growth we find that from 1500 to 2000 pounds per acre represents the annual increase. Hence we may readily deduce what minimum value is here to be applied to the general acreage.

If our 980,000,000 acres of farm land is given to nothing else than forest, we can harvest approximately one billion tons of wood products per year.

THE FARM CHEMURGIC

From our cultivated land we take somewhat over 400,000,000 tons of products; and really little use do we make of the rest of the farm acreage. Our trouble therefore lies in the disuse of enormous acreage or in allowing about 600,000,000 acres to run to waste. Even at so low an estimate as 50 per cent of average yield this neglected acreage left to itself under rain and sunlight should produce 300,000,000 tons of organic material. Taken then together with the tonnage of products from the cultivated land we ought to produce not less than 700,000,000 tons of agricultural products, which is a little more than 200,000,000 tons in excess of present returns. This calculation checks well with that result attainable if we were to make good use of all of our 360,000,000 acres of tillable land of which little more than half is now scarcely productive.

Belittle such calculations as we may, the four horsemen still hold sway. The soil is teeming with humus and microscopic life; the air is prodigal to excess with carbon dioxide; and the rain and sun give no sign of failing. Living matter must come forth!

In spite of protests and lamentations the insect world is fast encroaching upon man's domain. These insects thrive on waste organic matter and naturally multiply more and more as man withdraws from the

CHEMI-BIOLOGICAL RECKONING

forests. Though bird life is the only sure means of combating these pests man's slaughtering instincts have well nigh eliminated this control. Rather indeed have we chosen to dig up more of the mineral to throw against the insect. Harmful as this procedure is for edible produce it is only of late that we have taken heed of our misdoings. And we shall make no real headway here till we go back to the land and raise the properly selected plants that are poisonous alone to insects.

Every time we choose to bring out some new invention we foolishly rush to the mines for our raw products. Naturally then we come to this enormous outlay of mineral output over against land output. Even this might be condoned if we would only strive to make use of an increasing proportion of organic chemical material,—much of which is now procurable in type highly resistant to heat and moisture. Lowered prices will follow an increased use of same and especially after scientific men have cast out from the high places all those pseudo-economists now preaching higher prices for agricultural products.

Coal and petroleum constitute the half of our mineral output. We may bring about a greater change, therefore, in this ratio of "mineral output" to "land output" if we supplant a portion of these particular raw products by agricultural produce.

THE FARM CHEMURGIC

Fortunately, too, these particular raw products are organic and more than likely will have good counterparts among the organic products of the farm. Needless to remark that coal and petroleum constitute a legacy to us from the flora and fauna of æons past. It would seem fitting, therefore, that we waste them not now in profligate living, but permit a reasonable carry-over for future generations.

If, for example, we could replace about 250,000,000 tons of the present mineral output by an equal quantity of farm output we should bring the present-day amount of the latter up to 750,000,000 tons and reduce the mineral output to the same figure,— 750,000,000 tons. For the execution of this shift a number of years, of course, would be required.

It is not unwarrantable to prophesy that eventually we shall come to a ratio of "mineral output" to "land output" of about 1 to 2. This prediction is based on the scientifically directed use of sunlight at little or no extra expense. It further insures civilization against the encroachment of countless insects and pests. It really makes for the continuation of a progressive people.

We have learned how recent indeed are the chemical interpretations of plant growth. It was the turn of the century that ushered us into organic technicalization sufficient to supply a synthetic fibre. In

CHEMI-BIOLOGICAL RECKONING

organic chemical discovery lies the fate of mankind. It is this that will make for conservation of natural resources. Though there is abundance of coal, petroleum, iron and other metals we need not feel constrained to use them up at earliest moment. It is far wiser to broaden industrial activities such that the new organic counterparts, originating on the farm, may come into the picture.

Herein lies the crux of the chemi-biological plan. Herein lies the means of diverting the industries toward agricultural products as ideal raw material. Of course only the lowest priced material can first enter into consideration. What folly then for anyone in governmental or other positions to preach higher prices for farm produce! From the scientific standpoint such preachings are decidedly unorthodox if not unholy.

As we measure the products of the farm, altogether organic, over against the products of the factory, now largely inorganic, we are impressed with the utter impossibility for years to come for the farm to gain more than an equal output with the mines. This is all to the side of prosperity. It is exactly what envisages a national cycle under control. Briefly stated it pictures a farm cycle in full operation and an industrial cycle likewise in full operation but making up in raw products from the

THE FARM CHEMURGIC

mines what cannot be supplied by a full running farm cycle.

At last we have a feasible plan for relief of agricultural and industrial distress. With the two component cycles of the national cycle in consonance and coördination every human effort must lead to definite progress for both. It is not unthinkable that our industries may require such increase in raw products from the farm that we shall be forced to import freely for food requirements.

We shall not have long to wait before this dream is realized. It will be a godsend to our farmers who thereby will have become drawn into the chemical industries, — the only hope for organic chemical products, — the only things that ever can be produced on the farm.

Thus we realize how futile have been the efforts put forth in the past by all good-intentioned leaders looking toward a solution of the farm problem. Their efforts generally have involved either increased export or reduction of farm produce. These we now see are precisely the two steps we must reverse. We must not export but we must increase farm produce. Such are the dictates of the chemibiological studies and such are prerequisites to industrialization of agriculture.

In place of recommending export of our farm

CHEMI-BIOLOGICAL RECKONING

produce it is at once our duty to recommend its utilization within industry itself. In place of cutting down crops we must increase crops to such extent that industry may acquire a constant and dependable source for needed raw material. There is no hope under Heaven for agriculture to over-supply industry when once industry adapts the new discoveries to her enterprise.

True this plan calls for decreasing somewhat the use of mineral resources. This, as before stated, stands the nation in good stead. If perchance it necessitates a slight shifting in labor population this shift will be in the direction of the farm. Bringing our citizens back to the country will make for a better life and one admirably fitted to the rearing of wholesome youth.

The increase in use of farm produce calls for closer and closer biological control. It is here that biology brings under intensive study the chemistry of life processes. Soil, wind, rain, and sun—the powers of this world—never cease to toil. Through these powers photosynthesis continues, in oxidation-reduction steps, to yield cellulose, starch, sugar and protein,—the structure of an organic world. In these complexes we have our being to live and labor; without them we vanish.

By chemi-biological reckoning our Ship of State is

THE FARM CHEMURGIC

listing badly—in treacherous waters with skies overhung. The mighty resounding of machinery has an empty ring as we see our Ship still moving in circles. Our people have rushed pell mell to starboard, as it were, all intent on greedy pursuits at quickest pace, no matter what the consequence. "Back to port and the farm" now comes the cry. The good Ship must be righted ere coördinated impulses from farm and industrial cycles can be delivered through mighty propeller shafts to the smoothly rotating propellers completely submerged.

In this shift of interests the people once more shall have the freedom of the Ship. Greedy interests must come under severest penalties and highest income taxes. Constructive enterprise must be glorified. Then will abundant opportunity for work greet us at every turn. Failing this, peace and contentment lie far asea; but gaining this, our Ship of State holds an even keel and is trim and ready to breast the worst of seas.

CHAPTER XI

Chemurgy to the Fore

THE rise of organic chemistry in the fore part of this century marks the dawn of chemurgy as applied to the farm. Chemurgy signifies an intelligent working with and for chemicals. Though perfectly applicable to inorganic compounds it will always be concerned chiefly with organic compounds for the simple reason that there are and always will be some ten times as many organic as inorganic compounds capable of existence.

In an earlier chapter we have seen how nature builds up her vast storehouse of organic compounds, inclusive primarily of sugars, fats, oils, starch, inulin, cellulose, lignin, proteins and so on. It is only within recent years that anything like uniformity and purity could be secured for basic chemical compounds of agricultural origin; hence the art and science of working toward the production of such material has made necessary a somewhat more embracive term;—such term is *Chemurgy*.

Chemurgy comprehends the whole of chemical manufacture. It not alone applies to the work of

THE FARM CHEMURGIC

man but likewise may apply broadly to the accomplishments of nature. Thus the growing of cotton is but the manufacture of alpha-cellulose by nature under man's supervision; a true chemurgical operation.

Chemurgy brings out in relief the correct interpretation of agriculture. No longer a pursuit to supply man with food and raiment, but a pursuit that shall bring into existence a vast array of chemical compounds to fit a myriad of ends. It presents the most fascinating of pictures and the most awe-inspiring of nature's wonders. The tearing asunder of composite matter, heretofore known and used generally under such prehistoric names as "corn," "wheat," "potatoes," "straw" and "wood" and the like, and the allocation of the several homogeneous components thereof under their proper and clearly defined chemical characteristics, opens up a new world to man. It is the alphabet of a new knowledge; a knowledge that nature is now to inculcate in man.

The discarding of those time-worn nicknames will help us to appraise more correctly the value of each and all components that lurk within the products of agriculture. Then as chemical methods improve generally we shall likewise improve those steps that lead to purification of such components; whose lowered

CHEMURGY TO THE FORE

cost naturally redounds to the advance of organic chemical industry.

Even the crudest type of natural organic waste may find service in some connection. The impregnation of wood flour with phenol-formaldehyde condensation intermediates leads directly to plastics that admirably replace old-time wooden combustible material. Now the lamination of synthetic plastics leads to sheeting of unusual strength. When again this lamination includes a layer of thinly rolled metal between the laminæ of synthetic plastic, we come to sheeting of tremendous strength and durability. In this we have the future of automobile body structure, and likewise of interior finish in homes. This is only one of a thousand instances that can be cited to show the drift from wholly inorganic material to organic material either alone or carrying a bit of the old-fashioned inorganic make-up.

Both the lignin and cellulose, out of wood, admirably fit into this picture of supplying organic raw products for fire-proof and resistant materials of construction. Ordinary glucose or grape sugar offers another and interesting possibility in this direction. Just because our grandparents entertained the notion that sugar was just a food, is certainly no reason for us in following a notion now thoroughly disproved. Sugar is an excellent building material; in the near

THE FARM CHEMURGIC

future we should be constructing water mains of plastics from this source.

The foregoing is illustrative particularly of the tree and its chemical future. In addition to the carbohydrates we are likewise to make use extensively of their degradation products,—the vegetable oils. We can grow these oils to our hearts' content. And now that sufficient chemical insight is at hand we should direct our efforts to their increased adaptations.

Now a further step in purification of wood for removal of gums and resins leads to newsprint,—the whiter grades of which compose our newspaper and book stocks. In recent researches in this domain, as concerns the use of our southern pines to replace the more slowly growing spruce of the north, Dr. Charles H. Herty, under financial support by the Chemical Foundation of New York City, has accomplished at Savannah, Georgia, what all newsprint men have avowed impossible.

Dr. Herty discovered that in slash pine of twenty years growth heartwood has begun to form and gum and resin content to increase. In younger slash pine there is found only about 1.4 per cent of resin which is no more than is found generally in freshly cut spruce of the north. Evidently then very young southern pine can replace spruce for manufacture of newsprint.

CHEMURGY TO THE FORE

The cost of manufacturing newsprint from spruce at $10 a cord is about $42 per ton whereas the same high grade newsprint can now be made from young southern pine, valued at $3.50 a cord, for something like $31 per ton,—all possible allowance made for all possible items of expense. With something like 25,000,000 acres of abandoned farm lands in our southeastern states there is thus afforded a wonderful opportunity to plant same to pines and reap a harvest each year per acre of two cords of pulpwood.

The world's annual consumption of all kinds of paper amounts to 18,000,000 tons; of this the United States consumes 12,000,000 tons carrying a value of $500,000,000. Of white newsprint this country annually consumes 3,500,000 tons carrying a value of $140,000,000. Strange as it seems two-thirds of this amount is imported. Think of the opportunity that lies here at our door, and we have been as dotards,—sluggish beyond the saurian.

The chemurgical development of newsprint from young pine opens of course the next door to chemically purified alpha-cellulose itself. Such cellulose can be equally well prepared from young pine as from northern spruce and its purity ranks with the best of cotton linter. We consume annually in this country about 6,000,000 tons of wood pulp; most of this

145

THE FARM CHEMURGIC

passes through purification steps to yield a high grade of alpha-cellulose. And 33 per cent of this wood pulp valued at $57,000,000 is imported! Yet in our back-yards, as it were, stands wood abundant to all needs!

In the young pine lies the future of the South. Here the chemurgical development of cellulose must ever surpass all other pursuits. It behooves us however to improve rapidly the purification processes such that the present price of four cents per pound will be far outdistanced.

Closely allied to cellulose is starch. In this we are able to secure a cost price today of about one cent per pound. This low price takes its basis in cost of starch from tapioca raised in San Domingo where an average yield of purified starch amounts to 2,000 pounds per acre. In the United States scarcely more than 1,100 pounds of starch is now obtainable per acre from corn, in which the starch is present to the extent of 30 pounds per bushel of 56 pounds of corn. Thus at one cent per pound the starch content of corn brings a value of 30 cents to each bushel.

The chemurgical development of starch on the farm has been making steady progress. Formerly the great proportion of starch in corn was simply got rid of by feeding this corn to hogs in order that they might break it down into fat. In the old saying of

CHEMURGY TO THE FORE

"50-cent corn equivalent to five-cent pork" it was clearly indicative that the farmer could get rid of his corn by way of the porker. Today lard is in no great demand, and fat hogs are less prized for meat by the epicure than leaner hogs; in fact lean bacon brings a premium. Therefore this old method of disposing of corn must fall by the wayside.

There are those who cannot understand how a farmer can sell at low prices and still profit more than if he had demanded higher prices. If, for example, a farmer takes his corn to a chemical processor and sells this processor at one cent per pound some 30 pounds of starch out of every bushel of corn and then hauls back home the remaining 26 pounds of gluten and oil press-cake left in each bushel, he will have in his possession all of the ingredients necessary for livestock feed. In other words the farmer will have sold about half of his corn at 30 cents per bushel and still be in possession of all of his corn as far as an active feed stock is concerned.

In the light of such transactions it will not be long ere the farmer goes thoroughly into chemurgical operations. He will cultivate a corn that yields a higher and higher starch content in order that he may reap greater profit from this chemical component. If again there arises an increasing demand for corn oil, of which a bushel of corn carries about 1.5

THE FARM CHEMURGIC

pounds, he will suffer this component likewise to be removed by the processor and afford him some seven cents additional revenue per bushel of corn.

In this example of oil removal from corn it would become necessary for the farmer to supply to his livestock some other oil-containing material. For this purpose nothing could serve better than the soy bean,—of 40 per cent protein, 20 per cent fat, 20 per cent simple carbohydrates, and vitamins A, B, and D, but practically free of starch. In the simple removal of starch alone from corn the vitamins are not lost with the starch and hence the essential factor for growth of livestock is always conserved in the corn press-cake.

All in all the proper chemurgical procedure is to grow and deliver starch where starch is needed and grow and deliver oils where oils are needed. By such procedure there is a perfect solution for the age-old corn-hog question. Expressed from an industrial standpoint we have at last a means of making the salable material cut down the actual costs on non-salable material or by-product such that when these latter enter the markets in improvised form they too will cut down actual costs on some other non-salable material or afford a direct profit on themselves.

The great value of starch lies in the ease with which it is hydrolyzed to sugars. These sugars, as

CHEMURGY TO THE FORE

previously discussed, are readily fermentable into ethyl or grain alcohol with loss of carbon dioxide. Now this alcohol is obtainable at low cost when chemurgy persists on the farm. Furthermore alcohol is simple of storage and thus makes possible the elimination of that variant in farm life,—the quirks of weather. In fact alcohol affords one of the best possible means given to the farmer for storage of marketable surplus from good years against the adversities of lean years.

Chemists observe a steadily growing use for alcohol in all walks of life. It enters into so many processes of manufacture that practically no chemical company can operate without it. There is now arising a growing demand for alcohol in blends with gasoline to give us a super fuel for internal combustion engines. A mixture of 10 to 15 per cent anhydrous ethyl alcohol in ordinary gasoline adds markedly to the combustion properties of such gasoline.

It should first be noted that gasoline itself is far from an ideal motor fuel. In fact one-fourth of it must be wasted in an ordinary automobile motor in order to get the remaining three-fourths to explode with any degree of flexibility to the mechanism. This leads of course to incomplete combustion for a portion of the gasoline such that the exhaust vapors of

THE FARM CHEMURGIC

an automobile contain anywhere from 7 to 10 per cent of the highly toxic carbon monoxide.

So great has become the danger of carbon monoxide poisoning to residents of cities that *Lancet*, the famous English medical journal, has called attention to increase in number of deaths in London due to thrombosis of the brain; especially is this found in men over forty whose blood, in taking up carbon monoxide from time to time, becomes more and more susceptible to clot formation. Frequent and prolonged visits to the open air of countryside are of course recommended.

That the atmosphere in our larger cities is approaching close to the danger point is revealed in data recently published in this country. Herein is shown the presence of two parts carbon monoxide in 10,000 parts of air collected on Fifth Avenue, New York City, during the busy part of day. The human being can tolerate an atmosphere containing four parts of carbon monoxide in 10,000 of air for only one hour; after this hour of exposure carbon monoxide becomes clearly recognizable in the blood stream and registers its presence through severe headaches for those so exposed. Thus shopping overly long in and about stores on a thoroughfare supporting heavy automobile traffic leads to poisoned blood and serious after-effects. No modern city per-

CHEMURGY TO THE FORE

mits its traffic policemen to serve long in such heavy traffic; their frequent and regular transfer to outlying districts serves as restorative measure for their health.

The rational mode of procedure of course would be to get rid of this carbon monoxide at its source. In experiments recently conducted at Iowa State College it is found that the addition of only 10 per cent alcohol to gasoline reduces by one-half the carbon monoxide content ordinarily found in exhaust gases from an automobile motor. In that alcohol in automobile motor, with proper admixture of air, is capable of being burnt almost to completion and still give flexibility to motor performance, we have here an ideal diluent for gasoline if we would avoid formation of carbon monoxide and favor a higher content of carbon dioxide and water in the exhaust vapors; this latter is a measure of complete combustion of hydrocarbons.

Just lately English chemists have demonstrated experimentally that the initial stage in combustion of an aliphatic hydrocarbon (of the class of gasoline) with air is an alcohol (that is the same hydrocarbon with one of its hydrogen atoms replaced by an hydroxyl group) and that the concentration of such alcohol increases proportionately to the pressure under which these vapors burn. The presence of an additional quantity of alcohol at the start, as is in the gasoline fuel, does not hinder the oxidation reaction but only facilitates it; furthermore as alcohol vapors can be burnt under double the compression possible with gasoline vapors we have an additional argument that will lead, through improvements in motor, to much higher compression motors than now are possible in our automobiles.

The addition of alcohol to gasoline serves somewhat as an anti-knock agent. In this there is little to be gained as with decrease in size of cylinders, necessarily to follow alcohol-gasoline blends, anti-knock agents will be in peremptory demand. Of noteworthy mention is the possibility that these smaller motors, operating under higher compression, may find their proper location at rear end of automobile.

Naturally the heat units in a quantity of alcohol, which is a monohydroxyl derivative of a hydrocarbon, cannot be as high as in the original hydrocarbon; ethyl alcohol burns with liberation of only about two-thirds the heat units liberated by gasoline. However this seemingly unfavorable factor is almost entirely lost when reference is made to its complete combustion in motor cylinders as against only three-fourths combustion of gasoline in same cylinders.

When an automobile is propelled by the combustion of gasoline containing 10 to 15 per cent alcohol

CHEMURGY TO THE FORE

its road performance is found practically the same as when gasoline alone makes up the fuel. A decided advantage, however, accrues to the use of such alcohol-gasoline blends in cars operated in cities; here the wastage of fuel, in starting and stopping of car, registers greater loss on the part of straight gasoline, with the result that 5 to 10 per cent greater mileage is recorded with same cars when supplied with the alcohol-gasoline blend.

There are many technical points that must be considered in looking toward the general adoption of alcohol in gasoline for automobiles. An anhydrous alcohol is essential for proper admixture with gasoline and further it is advisable that a third or blending agent be present. All of these points are simple of attainment and entail no appreciable expense. Suffice it to say that 21 countries have adopted this type of super fuel and all report encouraging results.

Our interest in this fuel is, of course, the possibility it carries for extensive outlet for farm produce. It is clearly demonstrable that a high starch content corn can be raised in this country and hence a higher yield of starch assurable per acre. The by-product from sugar factories likewise will enter this picture. Such waste fermentable into alcohol only adds to the revenue of all concerned and further assures cane and beet culture against uncontrollable season losses. We

THE FARM CHEMURGIC

may indeed call this alcohol-gasoline fuel *"Agroline"* as representative of a fuel from agricultural sources; a fuel guaranteeing prosperity to agriculture!

In sucrose we have one of the lowest priced organic chemicals obtainable in nature. With a price in the raw state of little more than what we assign to starch it reaches four to five cents per pound when refined. There is every reason to believe that we shall soon be hydrolyzing cane or beet sugar into its two constituents, glucose and levulose, and after separating and purifying the latter for a ready market we shall ferment the former, as left in mother liquor, into alcohol.

Too much emphasis cannot be given to the introduction of levulose as preferred sweetening agent for daily use in foods. This levulose, some 50 per cent sweeter than cane sugar, will make for a less quantity consumption of sugar generally and thus contribute to better health on the part of our citizens. In a short time we should be cultivating girasole (Jerusalem artichoke) direct for levulose. The tubers of girasole will yield per acre about two tons of this supreme sweet sugar.

The tremendous quantities of carbon dioxide evolved in these fermentation steps must call for large containers or storage wherever alcohol is made. Centers in farming communities will need to be

CHEMURGY TO THE FORE

set up particularly to this end. Later we shall employ this waste carbon dioxide in certain combinations with ammonia to give urea derivatives and hence rich fertilizers; all to be so converted directly at these farm centers by *Nomadic Chemical Processing Companies*. The saving in costs for fertilizers so made to include all manner of farm waste, such as straw, weeds and leaves, will be stupendous.

CHAPTER XII

Science at the Helm

WITH these amazing chemurgical opportunities in our grasp and the realignment of agriculture and industry close at hand there is a call for scientific leadership that assurance be given each forward step.

Fears beset us all as we contemplate the chaotic state into which we have drifted. Many decry our state as hopeless; they await only the final crash. Poor souls! They lack perseverance and courage and are all too prone to forget that darkness ever precedes the dawn; that in the beginning all was void.

What forebodings confront us arise from among us, as we note the apathy displayed by governmental authority toward scientific considerations and the resistance by some industrial leaders toward scientific installations. Political indispositions ofttimes discourage the best of men.

To the betterment of our body politic and to the proper dispatch of scientific policies it becomes necessary that science be given control. She must take the helm to steer our course. Poor humans that we are

SCIENCE AT THE HELM

there is no order in our make-up save as science bids us follow. Politically we lead each other, then are led, and finally are lost. Religiously we display deep emotion and fervor but cannot remember the golden rule. Science is the only mistress we will obey.

In defense of those policies that science holds before us it is fitting that we be made to understand the necessity of proper coördination between agriculture and industry as a *sine qua non* to progress and prosperity. Science henceforth will demand that all of our activities shall be adjusted in keeping with this coördination.

There are those who rebel at every innovation; these are the men who have become so instilled with greed that their only object in life is for the hoarding of gold and credit. In matters of finance these greedy Aaronites have operated to secure control of enterprise after enterprise and then have milked it to the point of utter sterility while leaving their fellowmen holding what is left.

The railways are illustrative of such procedure. In early days they were highly successful but failed to adopt that chemeconomic principle requiring a retirement of each bonded indebtedness within the span of twenty or twenty-five years. Consequently they have sunk into mediocrity. For much of this the state and federal authorities deserve a fair share of blame.

THE FARM CHEMURGIC

The advent of the automobile and motor truck was looked upon by the railway companies as an invasion of their territory and prerogatives. Instead of adapting this new motor power to their purpose, they suffered it to develop against them until today it threatens them with extinction. No one any longer doubts the greater efficiency of the internal combustion engine over the old-time steam engine.

In the near future the government will undoubtedly take over our railways, especially now in lieu of many loans advanced to them. This should be a happy day for the railway companies as in one fell swoop their holdings become tax free. Eventually the railways should be given back to private ownership and management, but a new type of management which makes transportation at lowest cost and highest service its sole business. The future of railway transportation at great speed, with no grade crossings, nor city stations, will make the best of bus and truck companies glory in the distinction and privilege of serving such systems.

Just lately we have heard of opposition brought to bear against the development of southern pine for newsprint. This is another illustration of the avarice that besets the old-time industrial leaders. In place of expending a goodly sum annually on their own researches these newsprint manufacturers chose to

SCIENCE AT THE HELM

feather well their own nests. Today their nests are disintegrating; tomorrow they will have blown away.

For fourteen long years, ending in December, 1933, this country was cursed with the "Prohibition Plague." With good intentions and noble motives we invited this plague upon us; thinking we could rid our people of the curse and venom of drink. Finally we lifted the plague and hope returns that the only proper way to rid ourselves of an evil is to educate our people against it.

Now the prohibition plague set this country back fourteen years in organic technical progress. So great was this setback that, as previously stated, the unusual advance in inorganic chemistry over organic chemistry threw our whole national mechanism out of kilter. What water is to the inorganic chemical world so is alcohol to the organic chemical world. It is absolutely impossible for us to advance in organic chemical operations without low-priced basic organic compounds such as alcohol. Hence to the lack of developments in simple alcohol manufacture do we attribute much of our failure of late in keeping agriculture up to the topmost rank. Alcohol today is in the ascendant. If we cannot educate ourselves to live properly amid a world of chemicals, inert or poison, then it will be a blessing to the world if we are got rid of at earliest moment.

THE FARM CHEMURGIC

The cost of alcohol will be ever down. We have seen how it arises from starch by the way of sugar at a price approximately twice that of starch, when carbon dioxide is left to waste. Today purified alcohol costs about four cents per pound (25 cents per gallon), but it will not be difficult to produce ethyl alcohol at two cents per pound when once the chemurgical development of starch is under way. Later we know that this basic commodity, arising from agricultural sources, will approach a cost price as low as one cent per pound, that is definitely under 10 cents per gallon.

Fermentation processes are just in their infancy. It is highly pleasing that we now are engaged in several types of fermentation in this country and abroad looking toward widely divergent end products. Among the cheap unsaturated hydrocarbons from cracked natural gas or petroleum is ethylene; a gas which when hydrated (through an acid) yields ethyl alcohol. Those who love to boast of organic chemical attainments have been heard to say that ethyl alcohol will be made more cheaply from ethylene than by fermentation. This will be true if agricultural mismanagement long continues. We hope, however, that science will gain control and that agriculture will be given her proper place. Then when agricultural products are produced in plenty, ethyl alcohol will

SCIENCE AT THE HELM

be procurable at a cost approximately one-half its cost from ethylene even when the ethylene is given away free. Nothing can ever beat a source from nature if this source responds readily to cultivation and is not highly contaminated.

The suggested use of ethyl alcohol in gasoline to afford a super fuel for internal combustion engines awakened a broadside of opposition on the part of some of our oil corporations. Here again is the old-time clamor of the greedy who fear ever for their own pocketbooks without any thought for the good of their fellowmen.

All those who give an honest trial to alcohol-gasoline blends pronounce them decidedly superior to straight gasoline. Furthermore, they will be improved when once they are in large use; to this trend we have explained there never has been a single exception in all scientific history. The first installations for mixing and delivery will be rather expensive, but what of it. It is high time that the government shall step in and contribute a few millions of dollars toward some enterprise which renowned organic chemists the world over are agreed will positively help all agriculture.

As a matter of fact the oil companies, for their own good and as a point of distinction from rapidly decaying railway corporations who failed to sense the

THE FARM CHEMURGIC

growing efficiency of automobile and truck, should devote their untiring energies to study and installation of alcohol-gasoline super fuels. They should make a start in the corn belt, next possibly the sweet potato belt would be in line; but start it at all costs if they would keep abreast of the times.

Little mention here need be made of the principal objections conjured up by short-sighted, prejudiced members of oil companies. The proof of "agroline" is in the machine. One smaller company now is actually selling a low grade of gasoline containing 25 per cent alcohol and charged with a nice lot of casing-head gas. Those who use it cannot distinguish it from standard brands. The presence of alcohol here makes for a greater solubility of gaseous hydrocarbons. Hence this little company that keeps its eyes and ears open and mouth closed is able to market what the big companies are unable to sell.

This all goes to prove that the oil companies have yet a few years to wake up. It is a chemical world and we are to be under real chemical control. Agriculture must have an outlet for more of her organic chemicals and alcohol is the one and foremost that she ever will have. There is another organic chemical that likewise can be procured by degradation of agricultural products. This is the hydrocarbon methane. Its use would afford excellent lighting on the farm.

SCIENCE AT THE HELM

Its preparation and storage as yet offer a number of complications; hence that cheap organic degradation product, ethyl alcohol, claims our first recognition.

The sad part of our story now confronts us. In this country we have been producing annually about 100,000,000 gallons of alcohol; under stress we could double this production with our present equipment. Yet even with a 10 per cent addition of alcohol to gasoline we should require 1,600,000,000 gallons of alcohol for this country's use. This means the construction of ten times as many alcohol plants as are at present producing. This means the fermentation of 700,000,000 bushels of corn.

It is interesting to contemplate what conditions would face us if we were to use a 50 per cent content of alcohol in our gasoline, with proper modification in carburetor, of course, installed. The requirements for such mixture would be about 10,000,000,000 gallons of alcohol. On a basis of 2.5 gallons of alcohol from each bushel of corn there would be needed 4,000,000,000 bushels of corn, or almost double our present corn crop. On the basis of an average yield of 25 bushels per acre this would indicate that 160,000,000 acres of land must be cultivated to corn. This, of course, is almost half of all our land under cultiva-

THE FARM CHEMURGIC

tion but it represents almost the whole of our land that could produce even a fair yield of corn.

If now we seriously undertook this great enterprise and aimed to procure 10,000,000,000 gallons of alcohol by chemurgical developments on the farm, we should require the following set-up: One-half of our oil companies (involving 100,000 employees) would necessarily enter alcohol manufacture but at plants widely distributed over the country; their number of employees would need to be increased several fold. All available individuals of our 10,000,000 unemployed would be required to move to farm lands. And even with this vast additional help our farmers could not accomplish the necessary tasks save by working overtime and in all spare patches, railway rights-of-way, and vacant lots. In fact, several years would elapse, under this forced cultivation of land, before we could secure anything like the requisite annual output of starch and fermentable carbohydrates.

The remaining half of our oil companies, in turn, would be required to run at full speed in order that gasoline, lubricating, and fuel oil requirements be met; assuming, of course, that one-half of the present production of these hydrocarbons may remain as minimum. This supposition, however, is highly untenable. Within only a few years of the inauguration

SCIENCE AT THE HELM

of the project we should require as hydrocarbon component in this 50 per cent alcohol-gasoline blend as much gasoline as now consumed,—not to mention a greater demand also for lubricating oils which, however, by that time may also be coming directly from vegetable sources.

It is highly problematical that we, who boast of our success in mammoth projects, could succeed in the general introduction of gasoline carrying a 10 per cent content of alcohol short of five or ten years. It would require the greatest of skilled chemists and engineers. The first and greatest essential would be the proper location and distribution of the alcohol plants such as would reduce to a minimum all transportation charges on the corn, sweet potatoes, and starchy produce. The next and highly important factor would be the contracts to be drawn up with all farmers in the neighborhood of the alcohol plants, such that the sale of their entire output of carbohydrates, under intensive cultivation, could be guaranteed by contractual agreements with these alcohol companies. The prices of carbohydrates, of course, would be the lowest possible. But to compensate for low prices, the alcohol companies would guarantee also to the farmer a certain proportion of the net profits accruing to these companies, and subject to disbursement to each farmer on the basis of his

THE FARM CHEMURGIC

aliquot share in total carbohydrates fermented by alcohol plant in one season.

The government can well afford to center its whole means of recovery on this one project alone. No other project as yet suggested, outlined, attempted, or executed, can hold a candle to the alcohol in gasoline project and its future upon civilization; and all we need to start it is the removal of state and federal taxes upon agroline motor fuel for a period of three to five years!

If by a mere subsidy of a few cents per gallon on alcohol made to enter the motor industry we can launch an enterprise that bids fair to outstrip the great automobile industry itself—then Heaven grant us just a few years of such subsidy!

The gist of the whole problem is "constructive work and profit for all," and prosperity ever abounding. More automobiles and tractors will be built and sold and still more gasoline required than our visionless oil company executives can picture in their most exultant moments.

Is there anyone who cannot see how distorted our farm and industrial cycles have become? We have here the means of intensifying farm production with somewhat lowering of consumption out of natural resources. Of course no one looks to see the total

SCIENCE AT THE HELM

substitution of gasoline by alcohol for internal combustion engines! Alcohol alone would not be an ideal fuel any more than gasoline by itself! But in this move we have the secret of staving off what our farmers today are quietly striving to attain; namely, the replacement of gasoline-powered machinery by horse and mule power.

The farmers now realize the wreck that came upon their farm cycle. They should be commended for their intensive efforts to increase the breeding of horses and mules as now apparent all over this country. Will the oil companies sit idly by and see their gasoline fade out of the picture? Or will they awaken to the wonderful opportunities that confront them and work with the farmer to the ends that promise greatest good to the greatest number? Though the farmer now uses about 40 per cent of all gasoline consumed, we are confident that as a class he will be using 60 per cent of all agroline produced. This simply means that over 60 per cent of our population will be back on the farm within two or three years more.

Nothing is so to be regretted as the writings of medievalists—some apparently alive today (though dead chemically)—portraying the utter impossibility of agriculture ever being able to supply the fuel

THE FARM CHEMURGIC

requirements of this world when once the petroleum fields are depleted. As a matter of fact, this country can easily supply all of our fuel requirements from our waste lands alone. Vegetative growth now utilizes but a very small fraction of the incident sun's rays falling on the land. This proportion can be stepped up enormously. Today a mere 25 bushels of corn constitutes an average yield per acre; tomorrow we know how to bring this yield up to 200 bushels per acre. And when we introduce scientific air control, then will come a luxuriance of growth and such profusion of chemical products as will astound the most ardent. Particularly as a fuel source locale, the tropics, of course, will take precedence.

Taken together,—the new developments in utilization of pulp from young pines; the projected use of levulose; the introduction of alcohol in gasoline for automobile; and lastly the substitution of laminated synthetic plastics for steel construction of certain types,—we have four of the greatest immediate assurances for our glorious future. Most promising also is the development of soy bean and other oil-producing plants. Wherever there is a possibility of introducing on the farm that which enters more specifically the industrial field as against the comestible field, there we have the secret of reëstablishing

SCIENCE AT THE HELM

prosperity on the farm. This is the correction made necessary by the chemical revolution.

All of these things engage the farmer more and more extensively in chemurgical operation; all of these thus contribute to bringing the farm and industrial cycles under mutual control and under proper scientific direction at the helm.

CHAPTER XIII

The Old Order Changeth

UNDER scientific control there arises a greater and greater need for constructive enterprise. For years we have been given too much to looking for subsistence at the hands of the central government; till today practically 16 per cent of our entire population derives income from this central source. Only a decaying economic system could lend support to such wastage. In spite of evil forebodings let us hope that the treacherous and tyrannical bureaucracy it is certain to establish will not carry the germs of internal disintegration.

We do not advocate the dismissal of economic and political policies. There is need for such in their place. We insist now that all such activity play a secondary rôle where physical, chemical and biological factors come to the fore. The undue prominence accorded many of our statesmen is not begrudged; but let us not suffer the nation to drift during our zeal and enthusiasm for some unknown and unsung patriot.

We well recall the days of feudalism, when some

THE OLD ORDER CHANGETH

feudal lord atop a tiny hill was master of all he surveyed. In later years, even down to the close of the chemical revolution, business leaders had preëmpted the position of these erstwhile feudal lords, but for their own protection had become organized under political units known as nations.

Now the beginnings of science were fostered by many of the feudal lords, till they in turn gave way to better organizations; so too much of the discovery and advance of today has been fostered by industrialists as well as by government. Now in turn our industrialists must give way to better and more secure organizations that will make for extended industry under a firmer and more able government.

In other words banditry has served its day. We cannot continue as a nation where some live by plunder, others by alms, and still others by the keenness of their wits. Reason and intelligence must be enthroned; science must be our guide.

In the frontier days of this Republic when surplus in population moved ever to the West, we cleared the land and organized sections thereof into minutiæ called *Townships* of which a score or more made up a *County*. That village near the center of the county was called the *County Seat*. By horse and wagon the distance from any farm in the county to the county seat and back again consumed the better part of a

THE FARM CHEMURGIC

day. Thus each county organization had jurisdiction over a sufficiently large tract of land and its occupants as to make for ready and rapid daily transaction of all local business affairs. Beyond the county and embracive of a hundred counties more or less we come to the *State*.

Consider conditions today within one of our average-sized states. The advent of the automobile has made possible a rapidity of travel such that no county seat, in point of time, is more than 30 minutes distant from any of its outlying farms. Expenditures, therefore, in erection of courthouses and county buildings—and for maintenance of personnel attached thereto,—have become altogether unnecessary.

It is here that we must have a melding of a large number of counties to constitute a district or province within a state. Thus in Michigan the 15 counties of the upper peninsula may be organized under two districts; and the 68 counties of the lower peninsula may be organized under four or five districts.

It is asserted, on good authority, that were the State of Michigan to revamp her counties and countless petty offices under such broad and serviceable groups there would accrue at least a saving of $25,000,000 per annum to the state. This trend is before us and the longer we put off correct organization

THE OLD ORDER CHANGETH

under scientific direction the more will each and every citizen suffer.

Inertia on the part of our citizens is, of course, the answer to delay in such a simple matter as collocation of counties within states. Then, too, the revenue and fanciful political influence that will be lost to each county officer! How long will small fish in a small pan be able to resist scientific demands? Not long when they learn of what is coming. Whatever agitation we hear today advocating temporary withdrawal of right of franchise or suffrage from political office-holders during their terms of office may be forgotten in the light of a coming scientific régime.

Due to our industrial superactivities all efforts have been directed toward the manufacture of all manner of contrivances and sale thereof as rapidly as possible to our citizens. In their scramble over each other the manufacturers have not sensed that the purchasing power of a people depends directly upon their employment. When unemployment becomes apparent then purchasing power wanes and, on the part of those thrown out of work, there is a more urgent solicitation for every sort of federal, state, county or city office be it ever so petty, as of course most of them are.

The revolutionary change that science now brings to us opens a tremendous field of activity. Think of

THE FARM CHEMURGIC

the alcohol in gasoline alone that would require the constant attention of millions of men. Think of the wood pulp industries and the other industries emphasized in the preceding chapter. When we start these big enterprises in a big way there will not be a bystander on the streets of city or village out of work unless he is so obstinate as to choose so to be.

Let us not forget the petty officer in some old-fashioned county building. How long will he rest with his feet in mid-air and his nicotinized brain just able to understand the great chemurgical trend? Exuberance of spirit may yet arise within him; he will be off to the country and the open air and the open life and just rewards. And there will be vacancies in the offices of the county seat! One by one they will go, never to return to a deadened life and deadlier future. Theirs will be the work of chemurgists and theirs will be the life of content. To the physically invalided will belong the clerical positions that once supported unawakened youth.

The quest for good farm lands will become general. The study of soil will arouse the interest of our best citizens; through this will they come to know the power and resourcefulness of one of the four horsemen. Even where land has long been classed as submarginal these newly inspired men will be able to cultivate it to good advantage and to rich harvests.

THE OLD ORDER CHANGETH

In the sale of raw products to industry these students of the soil will be assured of good and reasonable profit in the open markets or on contractual agreement with some particular industry. Is there any likelihood that such men, enthralled with the workings of nature, will ever return to petty offices primarily suited to the physically incapacitated? Certainly not.

This projected extension of chemurgical activity meets little encouragement when we ponder the futility of man in his attempts to control another of the four horsemen of this world. The failure of man to conquer rain and snow stands as his greatest dereliction. We have a precipitation of two to three feet of rain per year and never should have any such thing as drought. This thing called man has built a few dams and made possible the beginning of irrigation. But what has he done to provide water to all purposes?—Nothing.

After all, what a helpless thing is man! Waters abundant to every purpose flowing downward to the sea! Millions expended here and there to conserve moisture in the soil, yet totally oblivious is this man to the applicability of a simple pump that will distribute the water everywhere! There's no need of our pouring valuable river water into the oceans and then sit in sackcloth and ashes praying that some stroke of fortune, as rain, will come along to bless us; such is mockery of nature to the last degree. Heaven is about tired of blessing such nincompoops.

In that soil with living vegetative cover loses moisture more rapidly than open water surface, and forests in particular contribute the greatest quantity of moisture to the air, even though they likewise consume sometimes almost the whole of the annual precipitation itself, we may visualize the future of our central states or those lands lying east of the Rocky Mountains. The prevailing summer winds over the central states come from the south and southeast; and about three-fourths of their total annual rainfall occurs in summer. What copious precipitation they will enjoy in the granary belt when we have begun the growing of pines in the southeastern states for wood pulp and the cultivation of lesser plants in Texas to chemurgical ends! The waters of the Tennessee and Mississippi can serve no greater purpose than in the irrigation of southern lands!

Recently announced plans of the federal government to plant in the mid-western states great strips of land to trees, such that these tree hedges will conserve moisture and arrest westerly winds, is indeed highly commendable. But this is a mere beginning. Scientifically speaking, the correct procedure would first call for construction of long strings of lakes

THE OLD ORDER CHANGETH

bordered by shrubs; later, perhaps, tree hedges may take hold,—but not till after the lakes are established. We must resort to every conceivable scientific means if we would avert the calamity that now threatens, and actually forestall the passing of our mid-western prairies into a Great American Desert!

In irrigation it is not enough to dig a trench and let a little water roll along to some field. True, this helps; but any child biologist knows it is not the correct method for supplying water to growing plants. In fact, by this prehistoric procedure, most of the water rapidly finds its way back into the rivers.

The real forward step in irrigation will follow the use of pipes running along over the fields preferably at elevation. By release of water from these pipes a spray will moisten the growing plant as well as the soil and only to that extent needed by that plant that particular night.

What kind of parent would place before his child the whole of a week's rations in food? These plants can synthesize only so much per day and any excess of water is just as bad for them as excess food for a human child. Witness how the stomata of green leaves are judiciously provided by nature with means for controlling intake of water!

On some of the Hawaiian Islands, where sugar cane is grown on the arid side of an island, water is

THE FARM CHEMURGIC

transported to this locality through ducts from the other or moist side of mountain island and allowed to come into the sugar fields at intermittent but properly adjudged stages of sugar cane growth. The sugar content of the cane so grown is enormously increased. In general such scientifically grown sugar cane carries three times as much sugar per ton as is found in sugar cane as ordinarily grown in the West Indies! An excellent example is here afforded of scientific method in chemurgical operation.

When at last water shall be under constant supply to all sections of our country then we can boast of ourselves as scientific engineers—and not till then. Nature constantly supplies all else to the living organism—but water comes only intermittently. She left this one horseman for man to direct and control. So far he hasn't advanced much above the ancient Sumerians. The few dams already built are worthy of notice but what are they compared with the million dams he has yet to build in this country!

The new scientific irrigation awaits the new synthetic plastic pipe. Pipe so cheap that miles of it cost but a few dollars. The steel industries will do well to enter this field. Today over 50 per cent of our steel finds its way into the automobile industry; and the very thought that here too, more than likely, laminated synthetic plastic may replace ordinary steel in

THE OLD ORDER CHANGETH

much of automobile construction, rests not lightly upon the minds of our so-called steel giants.

For the present the higher cost of laminated plastics will militate against their extensive adoption. However, cellulose and lignin are destined to enter this field and thereby provide us with plastics at very low cost. Particularly noteworthy here is this proposed utilization of by-products from the farm; thus making possible a general lowering in selling price of agricultural staples! Manufacturers of steel may scorn these suggestions, but if there is courage and valor within them they will put their houses in order to enter this mighty industry-to-be.

Imagine a bundle of wire and a lacing machine, a cauldron of synthetic plastic and a compressing apparatus. Then a ditch digger and a pliable last within a pliable cylindrical mold. As the wire intertwines itself into the form of pipe, synthetic plastic engulfs it and pressure sets the whole to continuous pipe,— a pipe just as long as the supply of materials determine its length to be. This is nothing but the laying of pipe with the speed and aid of a tractor.

Whatever changes are instituted in automobile construction make welcome news to our citizens. They are always glad to secure the latest models at lowest costs; and demand the best of workmanship. The newest cars will require less labor in construction

THE FARM CHEMURGIC

when once the moulding of synthetic plastic bodies enters the picture.

The possible reduction in demand for steel for automobiles does not necessarily signify a falling off in use of steel generally. True, this latter implication is more than justified when we realize the rapid advance now being made in light metal alloys, notably among which stands dowmetal as the lightest of metallic alloys ever capable of being made by man and stable under atmospheric conditions.

But the retrogression in use of steel for automobile will undoubtedly be made up by a progression in its use for home building. Here is an unlimited opportunity for steel skeletal structures. Tile, brick and other outside facing will be accompanied by lacquered wall board or synthetic plastic, as interior. Why should there be used anything of raw lumber in the construction of buildings? It has little inherent value and only adds a disintegrating factor to all structures containing it. Witness the dilapidated, broken-down habitations of much of our population today. The sight of these is revolting to honest men.

The changes that are called for everywhere seem almost beyond the hope of realization. Comparatively speaking, the decadence of the past decade or two has no equal in downright neglect for a like

THE OLD ORDER CHANGETH

period in all history. During phantom prosperity days we tolerated the crumbling of our habitations and the weakening of our industrial, political and moral fibre. Adversity was laughed aside. Today we know it is here. Mankind is in the slough of despond and nothing save real scientific leadership can bring us out.

CHAPTER XIV

Clouds Roll Away

SO many changes and reorganizations within our structure may lead us to wonder how ever can these things be accomplished. It is only faint heart that ne'er can win. All things are simple when we purge our medieval minds of rancor and superstition; when we come together in mutual understanding; and when we have the will to do.

This grab-as-grab-can policy of modern man has led him into the depths of despair. Possibly it is the inheritance of that counterpart in primitive man:—wild and random adventure. With the advent of our new order "the spirit of co-operation" shall reign. The clouds and storms that have constantly beset us may now be dissipated and we shall look out on a sea of grandeur beyond compare.

In the entire personnel of our Ship of State each shall have his duties to perform. The old languid spirit of waste and idleness will have vanished. New enterprise everywhere entails no end of labor and activity; in this truly is the hope for human happiness.

CLOUDS ROLL AWAY

The element of profit is the impelling force that drives us forward and toward security for our families. This must not be destroyed. But profits for the few and slavery for the many sow the seeds of rebellion within any people. A glance at history affords ample proof of such unfailing disasters.

The organizations within our body politic must be so revamped as to eliminate all cause for strife and hatred among the employees and employers in any institution. Much have we heard of strikes among laboring men who are dissatisfied with their leaders. In the new order where work can be had by all at any time it is not likely that anyone will long continue in the service of those for whom he lacks esteem.

In order that a nation may be assured of the honesty of those who would employ, and the faith of those who are employed, there is nothing more gratifying than a willingness on the part of both to share in each other's success or sorrow. Many companies today have instituted a profit-sharing plan for their employers and employees such that profits over and above a certain figure are subject to distribution under stipulated conditions to these employers and employees. Rarely do we learn of internal disturbances in such exemplary institutions.

The principle here is of course the basic principle upon which all industry must operate. The new order

THE FARM CHEMURGIC

will demand such procedure. Money invested in our industrial organizations has much too long been construed as inviolate. Physical matter in this world possesses only a relative worth. The progressiveness of a company therefore is the only standard upon which an investment can be gauged. For this reason we reiterate that an industrial group that is not constantly at work in research to tear down its every effort is a decadent group of men. Their end is oblivion.

Again we recall the future fate of our railway companies due to their unwillingness to acquire and improve every new method of transportation. The same future is to await petroleum and steel companies if they do not grasp alcohol fuel and synthetic plastics respectively. It is the fate of us all when we become so dumb we will not learn.

Thus as our investments are only of relative value within a company, and the success of that company hinges upon the consummate skill and management within the personnel thereof, it is entirely within reason that the employees as well as employers shall be rewarded proportionately to those who have committed themselves financially to this enterprise. The so-called profit-sharing checks answer this requirement to some extent.

Lately we note how leading industrialists are in-

CLOUDS ROLL AWAY

stituting group insurance for employees such that at least one-half of the carrying charges is borne by the particular company and the other portion by the employees. Then, too, various forms of insurance against possible unemployment are being introduced.

But all of these praiseworthy innovations are not yet sufficient to the ends sought. Whatever dividends are to be disbursed by an industry to its stockholders should carry at least 10 per cent of such disbursement to the group made up of employers and employees; in stock dividends this fractional quota may well constitute a sinking fund against retirement pension. The exact proportion will depend of course upon total payroll as against total evaluation of the corporation. Such *"Wage Dividends,"* as they may be called, would naturally supplant any profit-sharing checks.

The earnings of a corporation rest in large measure upon the intelligence, energy and craft displayed by the employers and employees. The hearts and souls of these men are wrapped up in the enterprise and its success commands their acclaim. In the continuance of a successful manufacturing industry the maintenance of an efficient personnel is just as valuable as the maintenance of the physical plant itself; disturbance in personnel is just as detrimental as the wreck of some physical set-up. Thus by wage divi-

THE FARM CHEMURGIC

dends we come upon a means of prorating earnings directly in proportion to investments. The wage earner loses all resentment toward those more abundantly blessed with worldly goods as he recognizes his earnings are in keeping with his own investment, that is his life and work as appraised by the particular industry. His dividends are in proportion to his investment.

Where wage dividends can be instituted there will be little recognition of outside disturbing agencies. The employees in particular will resent all interference from without. They will protect their source of dividend just as they protect their own families. It must be understood of course that a cut in salaries and wages makes obligatory a proportionate reduction in dividends and vice versa; whereas an increase in dividends will benefit employer and employees even though salaries and wages remain unchanged. With the chief incentive to strikes eliminated, strikes will be unknown; one can scarcely imagine even a dumb animal biting the hand that feeds it.

The inauguration of a spirit of good will becomes everywhere apparent when once this form of recognition of additional income is at hand. Such recognition will merit all the praise it is sure to receive. In this we have the clarification of personal relations between those who have money to invest and those

CLOUDS ROLL AWAY

who labor to make that investment safe and profitable.

During recent years we have witnessed a considerable drop in the purported values of securities. This drop of course had need to follow skyrocket values! In the subsequent falling markets many plant installations were closed down and the personnel highly demoralized. Today we witness a return of certain securities to values above 1929 levels. These are the securities of organizations that strive to progress over the wrecks of earlier achievement; in the main they are the chemical companies.

When future investors weigh well the two prime factors in an industry,—personnel and mechanical set-up,—they will not be so prone to study "book values." If they choose to cast their lot with the up-to-date industry they will insist that the net earnings of such industry be shared between those who place their lives and all in its service and that which runs the way of all wheels. The selfish and miserly investor has always recourse to Government bonds wherein the personal equation is absent.

It is to the ideal investor then that we look for the incentive that will bring industry itself to its senses. As scientific guidance dominates an industry so shall men rush to invest their earnings in securities of this scientifically managed organization, and particularly

THE FARM CHEMURGIC

when it becomes known that the supporting community shares a sympathy of interests unbeclouded by the spectre of unemployment.

Unemployment itself is a dark and sinister cloud. It makes for crime and debauchery and lowers the morale of our entire citizenry. The shift toward the farm as source of raw material for industry will require an ever-increasing number of men in agricultural pursuits. Thus we shall be able to rid ourselves of this curse of unemployment.

Before the passing of our last frontier unemployment found its own relief in the westward trek. Today our best lands are occupied. So with most nations. Present-day civilization therefore is face to face with the indigenous output of nature within its own borders. Years ago the productivity of nature beyond the borders of occupied territory attained its own equilibrium over against the forces of this world. As man entered he destroyed and in every way disrupted those mighty powers that lurk within soil and water. Nature was deprived of her only means of building defenses against the powers of destruction. Today these equilibrial conditions are becoming more unattainable till man and nature are almost chemurgically incapacitated. This means a devastation of our central areas,—a driving back of

CLOUDS ROLL AWAY

man to the water's edge. It is ancient history brought down to date.

Again, in time, this prodigal man may advance into the interior. If he has not yet learned chemurgical procedure he will be driven back once more. Nature's laws cannot be spurned. Not until man is firmly established in the "water-control" stage of agriculture shall there be an end of drought and an end of national disturbances that arise from insufficiency in self-containment. Then and then alone will there be little fear of misfortunes and adversities.

Little difference does it make if our present industrial units do have the capacity for practically twice their output as of today. This extra or unneeded installation of their physical set-up may be considered as fully amortized. If now we can reincorporate all activities under the chemi-biological plan we shall not have long to wait that extra pressure to be placed on industry in supplying the wants of our 10,000,000 unemployed soon to be given purchasing power through agricultural employment.

In chemurgical development of our lands we discern the brightest rays of light; light that will dispel the darkest clouds of unemployment. The organic chemical industry promises ten fold that which the inorganic chemical industry can ever hope to be. In this promise we are to realize the fulfillment of our

THE FARM CHEMURGIC

dreams and the assurance that all men can work who will. Variety unlimitable is the characteristic of organic chemistry and variety is the key to enlightenment.

There will be found those who decry all that is organic. To these visionless unfortunates we would recommend a study of the soil and its countless living forms. All such work without discontent and without financial reward; they require the lowliest of foods, but an abundance of water. Thus the soil is on the side of organic chemurgical advance. The human being against the enzyme has little chance of success unless he brings the enzyme under his control; but under control, the wonders of nature unfold at his feet. It is as if a new civilization were about to be born. Subjugation of wild animals to man's ends opened the culture we know today. Subjugation of microscopic life is to open the culture we shall know tomorrow.

Chemurgically speaking, this is the way of all nature that we are about to tread. This one of the four horsemen commends itself to man's upkeep and up-building. We have only to co-operate intelligently and the future is secure.

With implicit confidence in ourselves and in our ability to direct these Heaven-given assistants, what fears need longer beset us? With aspirations bright-

CLOUDS ROLL AWAY

ened through chemi-biological insight already revealed, what doubts can ever depress us? Aboard our good Ship of State this is the light that instills within us the dauntless spirit that makes for any Fate. It is the light by which the Ship herself is conditioned and the clouds of doubt and uncertainty roll away.

CHAPTER XV

Full Speed Ahead

UNDER scientific control there must arise a welter of criticism from those who would wallow in the mire of yesterday. We look to education as the salvation of these sorely afflicted. In the end their resentment will be assuaged as they learn all is well and the good Ship moves steadily ahead.

It is as if we had been sailing the chemical seas without chemical chart for lo these many years since our foundation. So with other nations. Storms that broke here and there have been weathered well but the mighty storm of the World War rocked the structures of everything afloat. The propelling mechanism of our Ship was thrown out of gear.

The wrenching of this mechanism has come about through increased power applied to the industrial cycle and almost total neglect of the farm cycle; such indeed that the propeller activated by the latter has actually been running in reverse when not out of the water altogether. Naturally our Ship of State went into circular course.

Political leaders, economists and doctors of di-

FULL SPEED AHEAD

verse cunning have been called from far and near. These doctors are much divided among themselves. One class, intent upon agriculture, presents a group that would speed up this activity to point of huge export and another group of this class would limit agriculture to point of food supply. A second class would speed up manufacture and dump a lot of the finished material overboard. A motley crew of doctors to say the least!

For years now this strife between the fundamentalists, iconoclasts and opportunists has held sway. No one can refrain commenting upon the calmness and composure of our citizenry; nor upon the implicit confidence in our Commander-in-Chief. Surely the light that breaks through the rift in the clouds will bring a rosy tomorrow.

During the chemical revolution that coursed the entire seas there was forced upon us a knowledge that was chemical and one that strengthened us in combating many of our lesser storms. This was the power of nitrogen, when fixed, to accomplish much that was beyond our power in years gone by. The discovery of this simple process we view now as one of the greatest discoveries of mankind.

It is regrettable that so little use has yet been made of this power to furnish cheap fertilizer to the farmlands and thus assure luxurious yields for agricul-

THE FARM CHEMURGIC

ture. In other directions likewise do we find this negligence on the part of man; seemingly he is wont to let latent possibilities lie latent. Upon closer scrutiny this is found to come through corrupting influence of those who would exploit our mineral resources to the utmost and to their own personal gain.

The keen realization that we are of chemi-biological structure and are afloat upon a chemical sea is beginning to impress itself upon us. There are still too many among us who will not see; their stubbornness and ignorance avail them naught. The money they have invested in decadent projects is lost. Is it possible that they would lose more just to keep some fatuous fancy free?

It is not at all impossible, ere our good Ship can be put in seaworthy condition that a whole generation of these misfit and ne'er-do-wells must needs have passed away. If such be necessary Heaven hasten their departure. We who would live by the sea must study and know well all chemicals above and below this ocean of water.

Albeit the heavens have been clearing and the waters bear a smoother surface. There is a rainbow in the skies and in translation of the colors there depicted we may read the promise to modern man:

FULL SPEED AHEAD

"Utilize all things to all ends but in proportion as *man* and *nature* produce."

Thus is given to man the secret of how to distribute labor scientifically among all trades. When human ingenuity invents machinery that renders more efficient certain steps in manufacture then the less skilled of labor that leaves this location must move down the ladder to positions making demands for lesser skill.

Eventually this labor will have reached the land where vigor builds up within them. The products of their toil in turn come back into factory. The greater the number turning toward the land the more of land produce must enter industry,—simultaneously the less of mines must enter industry. This creates the balance between agriculture and industry. It holds the ship on an even keel; and distributes power equally to our great cycles that drive the propeller shafts.

It is often said that one farmer can supply all the food requirements of five men in the city; undoubtedly so. But one industrially employed man can manufacture more than five times that quantity by weight which a single farmer can grow in the same year. Taken in the rough this ratio is indicative of the change that must be inaugurated ere we get agricultural and industrial commerce on a mutually inter-

THE FARM CHEMURGIC

locking basis. It gives us a rough picture of how it will become necessary to direct the unemployed into new channels necessary for production of raw organic material for industries.

To contemplate that necessary shift in population which would follow a governmental edict to the effect that only that quantity of mineral resources could be utilized in industry as corresponds roughly to one-half of the tonnage from agricultural sources is really startling. On present-day tonnage requirements we would need to force all of our 10,000,000 unemployed to enter farm service and furthermore would need to import an additional 10,000,000 laborers from abroad!

A greater number of men in agricultural pursuit will be required to supply that equivalent in tonnage which a lesser number can produce direct from the mines. And even though additional expense must be borne the increased demand for finished products so originating will fully compensate for extra outlay. In fact the increase in cost of various manufactured goods, which this push into remote districts for raw material entails, is the natural outcome of a scientifically correct plan; employment is made universal. Without this plan, and where unemployment persists, the federal government, as today, is forced to levy higher and higher taxes against all earnings of the

FULL SPEED AHEAD

people in order that construction in public works and labor-demanding enterprise shall afford work for all. The latter course stifles initiative, begets indolence, and builds for bureaucracy,—so inimical to American ideals.

As long as we do nothing for the unemployed but mete out relief, we virtually do them a harm. They must be given opportunities for real work. By education their morale must be maintained at highest pitch. Schools everywhere must be open to them. Now all of these things they can get on the farm. It remains only for the government to transport them farmwards as opportunities on the farms develop.

Possibly in time sufficient inertia will have been overcome that actual advance in accordance with scientific procedure can record itself. All we need is a nucleus; a starting point in some state here or there. Let that starting point organize itself among its citizenry such that correct discipline shall prevail; proper apportionment of men between agriculture and industry shall be determined by the commerce within the district. The rest takes care of itself. This plan calls for no expenditure of money whatsoever! But of course state and federal taxes will need to be removed from those products that have incorporated the required allotment of organic material.

For example the super fuel agroline, or gasoline

THE FARM CHEMURGIC

containing at least 10 per cent anhydrous ethyl alcohol and a blending agent, should be removed from all state and federal tax. This is the equivalent of placing a duty on some article whose manufacture in this country is to be encouraged. This exemption from tax should continue for at least five years. The immediate effect will be to encourage the manufacture of agroline and thus increase alcohol production generally.

In the same manner all automobiles, containing at least 10 or 15 per cent of their weight in laminated or other plastics, should be made exempt from taxation. The immediate effect here, just as above, will be to encourage greater production of plastics.

In general this plan involves the expenditure of not one single cent—how different from the jumble of discordant schemes we have about us now! The loss in state and federal revenues is no loss at all in the end; but if temporary aid must be forthcoming we have the sales tax to call upon.

Our best citizens are fully aware of the tremendous mineral resource strain that now persists. They realize too that farm resource neglect has brought us to this impasse. In chemurgy, then, we see the relief for the farm and the restoration to normal of the mine. This bespeaks the *Era* of *Chemical Dominance*.

If our citizens look not with favor upon this

FULL SPEED AHEAD

chemurgical development on the farm it may be left to our many industrial units to take over sufficient land for the supply of organic raw products best suited to each particular industry so choosing to expand. This corresponds to what is called vertical expansion of industry. By this means our industries can subvert that unscientific scheme that holds for higher prices for agricultural products.

The sad part of this alternative measure is the utter peasantry it holds in store for the farmer. His future will be far from rosy; his spirit of individualism and his initiative well nigh scattered to the winds.

Let come what may, we must not curb initiative. By initiative are we constantly reborn. In every way we should encourage all that attracts and leads man on. To do this there must be no regimenting of agriculture or industry. There must be no allotment plan nor any other type of planning that interferes with the capabilities of our citizenry. Balance the two great cycles, the rest is simple. What difference does it make if a farmer buys a new automobile each day so long as he sells plastic material per day sufficient to give him the purchase price of the car.

If there still be with us those who will not coöperate and who consider their will as law sufficient to all purpose, then slowly but surely they shall waste away

THE FARM CHEMURGIC

in vain. No man nor group of men can long withstand the attack of science and her followers. All things must work to the good of our Ship of State when once our citizens join in the teaching and effectuation of scientific principles.

In chemurgical sense it is highly criminal to cast aside that which nature brings forth freely and profusely to our service. To flout nature in the face is villainy even among nomadic tribes. Violators and despoilers of her bounties shall ever meet with retribution and dire adversity.

To incorporate daily with man's labor the concomitant produce of nature is to enter upon the *Era* of *Chemical Dominance* with banishment of the wild, reckless, resource-destroying policies of today. Beyond chemical dominance is yet biochemical dominance and beyond this still other stages of advance. Above all the edicts of nature stand immutable:—diligent, upright, and scientific man alone shall be preserved unto the age of enlightenment.

Political argument can serve no purpose to scientific order; etherial doctrines are without appeal; this chemical world is destined to continue as a chemical world. Chemi-biologically and chemi-biologically alone is it given to us to progress to higher and higher plane.

Thus will the good Ship plough ahead! By the

FULL SPEED AHEAD

Commander-in-Chief and crew stand an able corps of scientists and engineers. Evenly pulsating machinery in perfect gear delivers a world of power to propellers that whirl in rhythm with the great Ship herself. Constant scientific attention everywhere instills a confidence in our brotherhood and in the pilot who shall ever steer that course that leads to human happiness for all.